Volume 7
Frer/Gre

the world of automobiles
An Illustrated Encyclopedia of the Motor Car

COLUMBIA HOUSE/New York

Consultant Editor: Tom Northey
Executive Editor: Ian Ward
Editorial Director: Brian Innes
Assistant Editors: Laurie Caddell
Mike Winfield
Art Editor: David Goodman
Picture Research: Evan Davies
Cover Design: Harry W. Fass
Production Manager: Warren Bright

contributors
ANDY ANDERSON: Garlits
DAVID BURGESS WISE:
    Gardner, Goldie
    GAZ
    Gobron-Brillié
    Gordon Bennett Cup
    Gräf und Stift
    Graham-Paige
    Grégoire
    Grégoire, Jean A.
PAUL DARKE: General Motors
COLIN HAYNES: Ghia
BRIAN INNES: Friction
JOHN JAMES: Fuel Gauge
    Fuel Pump
    Gasket
L. J. K. SETRIGHT:
    Front-Wheel Drive
    Fuel
    Fuel Injection
    Gas Turbine
    Gear
    Gearbox
    Gravity
MIKE TWITE: Frère
    Frua
    Gardner, Frank
    Gearchanging
    German Grand Prix
    Gethin
    Gilbern
    Ginetta
    Ginther
    Glas
    Glassfibre
    Gonzales
    Goodwood
    Gordini
    Gordon-Keeble
    Graffenreid
    Granatelli
    Grand Prix
    GRD
    Green Monster
MIKE WINFIELD: Gregory

Picture acknowledgments
Page 721: Motor—722: Ferodo—723: Quattroruote—724: Martin Treadway Design—726: Renault; British Leyland—727: British Leyland; Renault—728: Martin Treadway Design—729: J. Bernardet; C. Pocklington—730: Quattroruote—731: Quattroruote; Quattroruote; Quattroruote; National Motor Museum—732: Quattroruote; National Motor Museum—733: Quattroruote; Frua; L. J. Caddell; AC Cars—735: Camera Press; BP—736: BP—737: L. J. Caddell; Time Instruments—739: Quattroruote; Chevrolet—741: P. Revere—742: P. Revere—743: National Motor Museum—744: G. Goddard—745: R. Phillips—746: P. Revere—747: Quattroruote; Alexander—748: G. Goddard—749: G. Goddard—750: G. Goddard; G. Goddard; British Leyland—751: British Leyland—752: Novosti—753: P. Tilley; Quattroruote—754: Papetti—755: Papetti; T. Nesta—756: Fiat/Quattroruote; Betti—757: Betti—758: T. Nesta—759: Mercedes—761: L. J. Caddell; D. Goodman—762: L. J. Caddell—763: Quattroruote; General Motors—764: General Motors—765: General Motors—766: Quattroruote; General Motors—767: General Motors—768: General Motors—769: General Motors—770: General Motors—771: Quattroruote—772: Quattroruote—773: Boroli—774: London Art Tech—775: Ford; C. Pocklington; C. Pocklington; C. Pocklington—776: Ford; Quattroruote; Quattroruote—777: Ford; Quattroruote; Quattroruote—778: Quattroruote; Quattroruote; Zagari; Quattroruote; Coluzzi—779: Zagari; Quattroruote; Quattroruote; C. Pocklington—780: Carpinacci; Ghia; Ford—781: L. J. Caddell; Cherrett; L. J. Caddell—782: L. J. Caddell—783: Cherrett; C. Pocklington—784: Cherrett; C. Pocklington—785: London Art Tech—786: London Art Tech—787: London Art Tech—788: G. Goddard—789: National Motor Museum—790: Molter; Quattroruote; National Motor Museum—791: C. Pocklington; Quattroruote; Quattroruote; C. Pocklington—792: Reliant—793: P. Revere; Specialised Mouldings—794: Specialised Mouldings; Specialised Mouldings; Reliant—795: Belli; National Motor Museum; National Motor Museum—796: Burgess Wise—797: Cherrett; National Motor Museum—798/799: National Motor Museum (I)—799: Popperfoto—800: Bonetto; National Motor Museum—801: London Art Tech—802: London Art Tech; Aerofilms—802/803: London Art Tech—803: London Art Tech—804: Bisconcini—805: Nesta; Belli; Bonetto; Phipps; Moity—806: Bonetto; Boschetti—807: Quattroruote—808: National Motor Museum (I)—809: National Motor Museum—810: National Motor Museum—811: C. Pocklington—812: C. Pocklington—813: National Motor Museum—814: Von Fersen—814/815: A. C. Cooper—815: Von Fersen—816: Popperfoto; Keystone—817: Quattroruote—818: Quattroruote; National Motor Museum; National Motor Museum—819: Quattroruote; National Motor Museum; National Motor Museum; National Motor Museum—820: National Motor Museum—821: National Motor Museum; Quattroruote—822: National Motor Museum; Quattroruote; National Motor Museum; Ferruccio Bernabo; Ferruccio Bernabo; Ferruccio Bernabo; Ferruccio Bernabo—823: Quattroruote; Ferruccio Bernabo—824: IGDA Orbis—825: C. Dani; IGDA; Falletti—826: Attualfoto—827: Phipps; Phipps; I. Ward—828: Quattroruote; 829: London Art Tech—830: London Art Tech—831: Ceci; London Art Tech—832: Quattroruote; Ceci; London Art Tech—832/833: London Art Tech—833: De Vita; London Art Tech—834: Quattroruote; Hot Car; Hot Car—835: Hot Car—836: Bisconcini; National Motor Museum—837: IMS; National Motor Museum; IMS—838: National Motor Museum—839: Quattroruote—840: London Art Tech; National Motor Museum

© Orbis Publishing Limited, London 1974
© Quattroruote/Domus, Milan & Instituto Geografico De Agostini, Novara 1974

Distributed by Columbia House, 51 West 52nd Street, New York, New York 10019
Printed in U.S.A.

Contents

Section	Title	Page
BETTER DRIVING	Gearchanging: Making Proper Use of the Gearbox	761
CARS OF TODAY	Ginetta G21	787
THE GREAT CARS	GAZ: Part of the Russian Revolution	752
	Gilbern: The Invaders From Wales	781
	Ginetta: Car Building—A Family Affair	783
	Glas: From Goggomobils to Grand Tourers	789
	Gobron-Brillié: The First 100 mph Motor Car	795
	Gordon-Keeble: A Luxury Grand Tourer	811
	Gräf und Stift: The Rolls-Royce of Austria	813
	Graham-Paige: American Motoring's Age of Chivalry	817
	Grégoire: The Company That Died With Its Founder	836
HOW IT WORKS	Friction: An Essential Yet Destructive Phenomenon	722
	Front-Wheel Drive: Putting the Horse Before the Cart	725
	Fuel: Life Blood of the Motor Car	734
	Fuel Gauge: A Measure of Consumption	737
	Fuel Injection: An Alternative to the Carburettor	738
	Fuel Pump: Supplying the Carburettor	741
	Gasket: Providing an Efficient Fluid Seal	746
	Gas Turbine: The Ultimate Rotary Engine?	748
	Gear: A Positive Link Between Two Shafts	754
	Gearbox: Multiplying the Engine's Flexibility	756
	Glassfibre: Bodywork for the Specialist	792
	Gravity: Towards the Centre of the Earth	828
THE MOTOR INDUSTRY	Frua: New Bodies for Old	729
	General Motors: An Industrial Giant	763
	Ghia: The "Dior" of Motoring Fashion	775
WHO'S WHO	Frère: Racing Driver Turned Journalist	721
	Goldie Gardner: From Brooklands to Bonneville	743
	Frank Gardner: King of the "Big Banger"	744
	Garlits: Drag's Charger	745
	Gethin: Famous Son of a Famous Father	774
	Ginther: One of America's Best	788
	Gonzales: The Wild Bull From the Pampas	800
	Graffenreid: The Epitome of a Wealthy Amateur	816
	Granatelli: The Flamboyant Mr. Indianapolis	820
	Grégoire: A Man of Many Talents	839
	Gregory: A Stranger in His Own Country	840
WORLD OF SPEED	German Grand Prix: The "Circus" at the "Ring"	771
	Golden Arrow: The Record-Breaker That Ran Only Once	798
	Goodwood: The Rise and Fall of Goodwood	801
	Gordini: The French Call Him "Le Sorcier"	804
	Gordon Bennett Cup: Forerunner of the Grand Prix	808
	Grand Prix: Motor Racing's Premier Championship	821
	GRD: Rise of the Phoenix	831
	Green Monster: High-Speed Monster	834

Racing driver turned journalist

PAUL FRERE IS A VERY RARE combination of racing driver, engineer and journalist. There are several drivers who have become successful journalists, a few journalists who have become successful drivers and several engineers who have become successful drivers, but very few combine all three talents with any effect.

Born in 1917, Frère spent his formative years living in Berlin and Vienna, spending only occasional holidays in Belgium, his home country. On some of his trips to Belgium, an uncle took him to the motor racing at the Spa-Francorchamps road circuit. This kindled his interest and his first competition event was in his mother's Amilcar, which he used to win a gymkhana in Austria. World War II postponed any plans that Frère might have nursed, but he spent most of the war in France working in a garage, gaining a great deal of mechanical knowledge.

After the war, he returned to Belgium and began racing motor cycles with some success, even capturing some world speed records in the 125 cc class. He turned to motor racing in 1948 when a friend, Jacques Swaters, asked him to co-drive his 1936 MG PB in the Spa 24 Hour race. The car ran almost faultlessly to capture fourth place in its class and rekindle Frère's enthusiasm for racing.

He had begun to make a name for himself in motoring journalism and, through the contacts he made while carrying out road tests and describing new cars, he was able to arrange various drives in saloon-car races. But between 1948 and 1951, he took part in only a few races, driving cars like the Dyna-Panhard and Jowett Javelin and his racing career seemed to stagnate. However, in 1952, he won the production-car race at Spa in an Oldsmobile and was later invited to drive one of the British HWM Formula Two single seaters at Chimay. Despite never having driven a single seater before, he picked his way through the field on the wet track and won in an exciting finish. He followed this with a fifth place in the European Grand Prix at Spa, in the same car, and then went to the German Grand Prix, again in an HWM, where he retired. The season ended with a drive in the Dutch GP in a Simca-Gordini, where he again retired.

In 1953, he won his class in the Mille Miglia, driving a Chrysler, following up with a win in the Spa production-car race in another Chrysler. He drove an HWM at the Eifelrennen on the Nürburgring, taking second place, and then finished second in class at Le Mans driving a Porsche. He drove HWMs in the Belgian GP and the Reims 12-hour sports car race with no success, but he was now competing regularly and was given a trial by Mercedes for their 1954 Grand Prix team, just failing to gain a place.

He started 1954 with a class win—once again in the Spa production-car race—in an Alfa Romeo, and drove an Aston Martin at Le Mans, where he was forced to retire. He also drove for the Gordini Formula One team on occasions, but the cars were unreliable.

Aston Martin signed Frère for sports-car

Above: Belgium's Paul Frère, Grand Prix winner, Le Mans winner and now one of the world's most respected journalists. Frère has been involved in motor sport since before World War II

racing in 1955, and he also drove the Super Squalo Formula One Ferrari at Monaco and Spa, finishing eighth at Monaco and fourth in the Belgian GP. In the Aston Martin, he co-drove with Peter Collins to second place in the 1955 Le Mans race, but he crashed a Monza Ferrari during practice for the Swedish Grand Prix and broke a leg, which kept him out of racing for the rest of 1955.

For 1956 Jaguar signed Frère to drive the all-conquering D-type sports car and 2.4 saloon, and he started off with victory in the 2.4 in the Spa production-car race, as well as winning his class in the sports-car race, driving a Ferrari. Ferrari also invited him to drive a Lancia-Ferrari V8 in the Belgian Grand Prix and, although he was reluctant to return to Formula One racing, he agreed and ended up by taking second place, to the great delight of his countrymen. He co-drove a D-type Jaguar with Mike Hawthorn to take second place in the Reims 12-hour race, but crashed on his second lap at Le Mans, putting both himself and team mate Fairman out of the race. He finished the season with sixth place on the Tour de France in an Alfa Romeo and third place in the Rome Grand Prix in a Ferrari.

At the end of the 1956 season, Frère decided that he would give up serious racing and concentrate on his journalistic career, but he continued to take part in occasional events when the opportunity occurred. In 1957 and 1958, he won the Reims 12-hour race with his countryman Olivier Gendebien and in 1959 he was invited to return to the Aston Martin team. His second place at Le Mans with Trintignant, and fourth place in the Tourist Trophy at Goodwood, helped Aston Martin win the World Sports Car Championship.

His final season was in 1960, during which he showed that at the age of 43 he had lost little of his touch even though he raced only occasionally, for he won the Spa sports-car race in a Porsche RS60 and, driving a single seater for the last time, he went to South Africa and won the South African Grand Prix in a Cooper-Climax, beating Stirling Moss, in a Cooper Borgward, into second place. The seal was set on his career when he won the 1960 Le Mans race co-driving a V12 Ferrari with Olivier Gendebien.

He retired for good after Le Mans, to concentrate on his journalistic career, although he was often invited to test racing cars. In 1974, aged 57, he had the appearance of a man of 40 and such was his skill, that whenever journalists gathered for a test session on some new model there was always a rush to fill the spare seats in the car Frère chose. MT

Friction/HOW IT WORKS

AN ESSENTIAL YET DESTRUCTIVE PHENOMENON

Applied in the right places, friction enables the car to be steered, started and stopped. Its application in some other areas, however, simply causes wear and tear

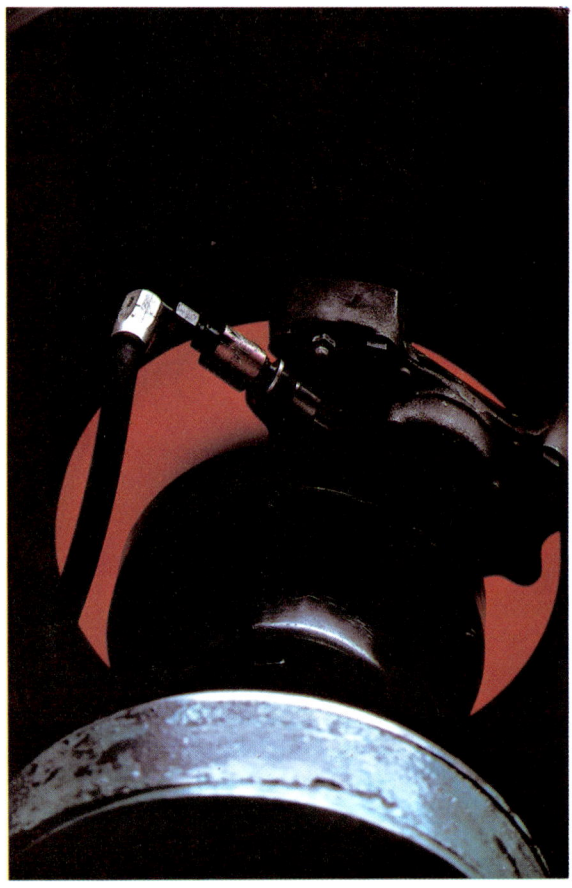

Right: in most automotive cases, friction is something which engineers strive to reduce, but there are exceptions, the brakes being an important one. Here, brake disc pads are being tested by Ferodo; the disc itself is red hot, but the pads are undamaged

Far right, top: another example of friction essential to the motor car is that between tyres and road. Formula One cars use enormous tyres in an effort to achieve a happy medium between maximum friction and minimal drag. This BRM P160 has taken a corner too fast and the friction between rubber and tarmac has caused the tyres to smoke

WITHOUT FRICTION our cars would run forever; indeed we should be unable to stop them, but for the fact that we would never be able to get them started. In the compromise-ridden world of automotive engineering, we content ourselves with trying to minimize friction in the engine, the transmission, the door locks, the screenwipers and all mechanical odds and ends; we even try to minimize friction in the air passing over the bodywork or through the engine's induction system, and in the gases negotiating the exhaust pipe; but at the same time every attempt is made to increase the frictional capabilities of the clutch, brakes, dampers and tyres. In the right place, friction enables the car to be started, steered, and stopped; elsewhere, it merely makes the thing wear out.

The so-called 'laws' of friction were first formulated by Leonardo da Vinci and established experimentally by the French scientist Coulomb in 1785. Frictional drag is determined by the nature of the mating surfaces and the force squeezing them together, and is not dependent on the area of contact—a brick dragged along a surface exerts exactly the same frictional force whether it is on its side or standing on its end. The friction F is proportional to the load W between the two surfaces, and the constant F/W is called the 'coefficient of friction' and is symbolised by the Greek letter μ or mu.

At first sight, one would not expect μ to exceed 1, because it seems inconceivable that the frictional force exerted by a body could be greater than its weight. This, however, does not take account of the peculiar nature of friction, and what causes it. Friction between rough surfaces appears to be due to the asperities of these surfaces interlocking, so that they engage in a manner analogous to the meshing of gears. So we find the μ of brake linings and pads varying between 0.25 and 0.5 according to duty—a given material producing somewhat different figures according to its temperature and rubbing velocity.

But friction between smooth surfaces is, paradoxically, much greater. The coefficient of friction between two polished copper blocks, for instance, lies between 0.8 and 1, and if the metal is cleaned so as to remove all traces of grease and oxidation, an even higher figure will be obtained. What has happened is that friction due to the minute asperities on the two surfaces has been overwhelmed by a process of interface bonding, so that local welds are created and then have to be torn apart.

In the case of tyres for the motor car, we find that the coefficient μ can range from 0 to 2.2. The zero coefficient was found during Dunlop's investigations of hydroplaning: when a tyre revolving at fairly high speed is isolated from the road by an intervening wedge of water, forming a lubricating film between the two surfaces, it can be stopped from rotating or even be made to revolve backwards without showing any tendency to resume its original motion. Bearings relying on rubber and water have already been tried for other applications (ship's propeller-shaft bearings, for instance) and the apparent negation of friction, theoretically an impossibility, may in time be exploited in dramatically important ways. No less dramatic are the braking figures measured in tests with racing cars and the tyres developed specially for them: retardations of 2.2g have been measured by Porsche and others. Tyres made of butyl (the synthetic rubber normally used for inner tubes) produced coefficients of 2 even on ordinary saloon cars in experiments conducted in the mid 1960s. Similar figures are realised during acceleration by the fastest drag-racing cars with their special tyres.

The rubbing and welding and tearing that occur between cylinder bores and piston rings create what is usually the largest source of frictional loss of power in an engine. To reduce the number of rings reduces this loss but increases oil consumption. The viscosity of the oil itself creates a drag that is measurable as friction horsepower: a leading designer of racing engines recently declared that the reduction of oil drag (by reducing the size of bearings, using different types of bearings, and generally minimising

HOW IT WORKS/Friction

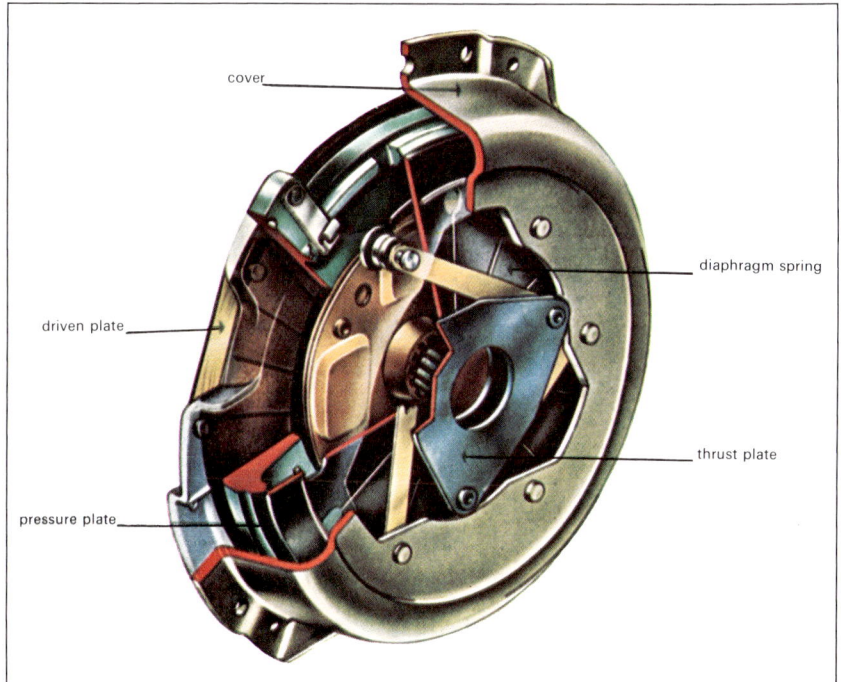

the resistance of oil circuits to the pumping of necessary lubricant) was one of the most important means remaining for the augmentation of engine power, now that most contenders are on equal terms in such matters as combustion chamber and inlet design.

Outside the engine and transmission, where fluid lubricants remain essential, much is being done to eliminate both friction and the need for oils and greases. Dry lubricants and plastic bushes and bearings, sometimes using low-friction materials such as polytetrafluorethylene (alias PTFE) or molybdenum disulphide (MbS_2) and sometimes simple stuff such as nylon (which is lubricated by water), play an important part in reducing friction and wear in suspension systems and minor components such as throttle linkages or door hinges. The elimination of friction from suspension systems is most important, for it modifies the behaviour of the springs in an incalculable way. To the known spring rate must then be added a 'parasitic rate', about which few designers seem to bother. The Moulton Hydragas system of the Austin Allegro takes it into account; the Bristol 410 and 411 had it painstakingly eliminated; but it would be a mistake to think that all the common rubber suspension bushes and the like in most cars help to reduce it. Instead the rubber suffers friction internally. So in fact does every piece of material, polymer or metal that is subjected to strain or distortion. BI

Above left: a cutaway view of a clutch driven plate which makes use of friction to transmit energy from engine to wheels

Above: a complete clutch assembly, a further example of a good use for friction in a motor car

Right: the front suspension and engine/transmission unit of the Triumph 1300, showing how the various mechanisms are integrated into a complete unit

Below right: an unusual view of a transverse-engined front-wheel-drive vehicle from the British Leyland range

Below: front-wheel drive has steadily been gaining popularity over the last twenty years, particularly with the European manufacturers. One company, that is no stranger to the layout is Renault which uses the system in its Renault 15 and 17 models among others

HOW IT WORKS/Front-wheel drive

PUTTING THE HORSE BEFORE THE CART

The idea of front-wheel drive was originally inspired by the horse and cart. Over the years the system has been developed and refined and is now enjoying great popularity

THE IDEA THAT THE FRONT WHEELS of a car might make a better job of pulling it along than the back wheels of pushing it, is little younger than the car itself, the inspiration coming from horse-drawn-vehicle practice in which the putting of the cart before the horse was axiomatically incorrect; the Cugnot steamer of 1770 was probably the earliest front-wheel-drive machine. Had the cart been furnished with more adequate steering mechanisms, and had the horse enjoyed periscopic vision, things might have been different. A number of front-wheel-drive motor cycles in production at the turn of the century gave advanced warning of the difficulties lying in wait for the car designer who would pursue the same idea. Nevertheless, by the 1920s, front-wheel drive enjoyed considerable popularity in sporting cars such as the Tracta and Alvis, and even in racing cars—especially in the USA, where the de Dion axle was brilliantly adapted by Miller to serve the driven front wheels of his Indianapolis racers. Indeed, the American speedway had been introduced to the idea as early as 1905, and Barney Oldfield piled up many records with his car.

Later in the 1920s, Harry Miller met E. L. Cord, president of Auburn, and from that meeting sprang the front-drive Cord car, a machine that somehow caught all the attention but dropped all the chances. The technical feature that was most significant in the Cord was a new kind of constant-velocity universal joint for the drive shafts. This permitted much greater angular displacement of the wheels for steering than had been possible in earlier front-drive machines, whose poor turning circles had given them bad names. The joints previously used were mostly of the common Hooke type, still to be found in the propeller shafts of most front-engined, rear-wheel-driven cars, and when a joint of this type is deflected, the speed of rotation of the output end varies cyclically, the amount of variation depending on the degree of deflection. This caused troublesome variation in the speed of rotation of the driven front wheels when steering lock was applied.

Complex double joints and other kinds were developed by the Frenchman J. A. Gregoire, progenitor of the Tracta, not to be confused with the American B. F. Gregory, whose front-wheel-drive designs inspired Miller; and it was largely due to Gregoire's perseverance that front-wheel drive eventually became a commercial as well as a technical success in France in the mid 1930s. The car that achieved this was the Citroën 11 Légère (known in England as the Light 15), which remained in production and in great demand until the mid 1950s. Early versions were not entirely trouble-free: the drive shafts were supposed to be greased every 500 miles. Nevertheless, the car flourished, and doubts about the practicability of front-wheel drive receded.

With the major mechanical problems overcome, the way was clear to exploit the system's undoubted advantages. The greatest of these had little or nothing to do with traction, being simply the elimination of the awkward propeller shaft which conveyed the drive from front engine to rear axle in conventional cars. With this shaft gone, the floor could be flat and the seats lower, allowing either more cabin space or a lower roof which, in turn, led to a reduction in frontal area and therefore to lower aerodynamic drag. With the shaft gone, there was less temptation on the part of designers to retain the conventional chassis, whose depth was always excusable on the grounds that the floor had to be that much higher anyway to clear the propshaft; so there was a strong case for abjuring the chassis and adopting the unitary type of pressed-steel stressed-hull construction gradually making headway among firms devoted to mass production.

Another advantage of front-wheel drive was the inherent directional stability it conferred. Such a car is naturally nose-heavy, with its centre of gravity well forward of mid wheelbase. Add to this the debasement of cornering power of the front tyres because of the camber changes induced by most of the independent suspension systems with which (outside America, at any rate) front-wheel drive was associated, and the further debasement caused by the sheer load on the tyres—which in those early days were skinny affairs that were run nearer their limits than today—and the result was a pronounced understeer that the fast but unskilled driver found very forgiving. Moreover—although the point was seldom appreciated before World War I—the forward location of the centre of gravity improved the chances of its remaining ahead of the aerodynamic centre of pressure, even in a well streamlined body travelling fast, so that the suspension-induced understeer was not overcome at high speeds by aerodynamically induced oversteer. Front-wheel-drive cars therefore acquired a reputation for exceptional directional stability in cross-winds.

Probably the real reason for the Citroën's ability to get an overweening driver round a corner and out of trouble was not that its front wheels were driven but that it was low, stiffly constructed, and very wide in the track, with minimal overhang at each end of a long wheelbase. With these advantages, it could hardly help but be stable and, indeed, a car of such width could have retained them even with rear-wheel drive. Nevertheless, it became accepted that driving the front wheels was a sure way to achieve outstanding roadworthiness and, while the man in the street has remained pretty well convinced of this truism to this day, the man on the racing track soon began to wonder why things did not always work out that way. Sundry small French sports cars puttering around the corners at Le Mans did not exactly encourage the pursuit of those ideas for full-blooded, front-drive racing cars.

Miller himself had said: 'I do not believe that the front-drive car is any faster than the rear-drive type. The reason why it can make better time on the speedways is that it is unnecessary for the drivers to slow down around corners, the skidding of the front-drive

725

Front-wheel drive/HOW IT WORKS

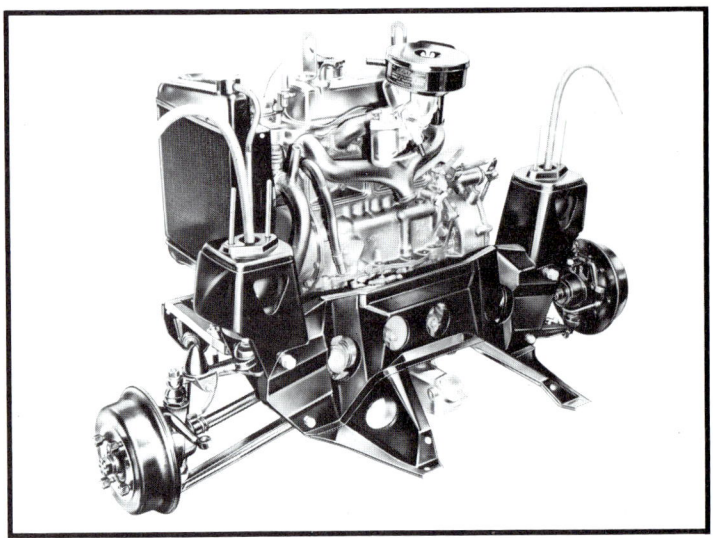

Above: the giant Volkswagen company caused a sensation in the motoring world when it introduced the new Passat model. The four-cylinder, four-stroke engine powered the front wheels, a major breakaway from normal VW practice

Above right: British Leyland's Mini is powered by a four-cylinder unit, mounted transversely across the front sub-frame, driving the front wheels.

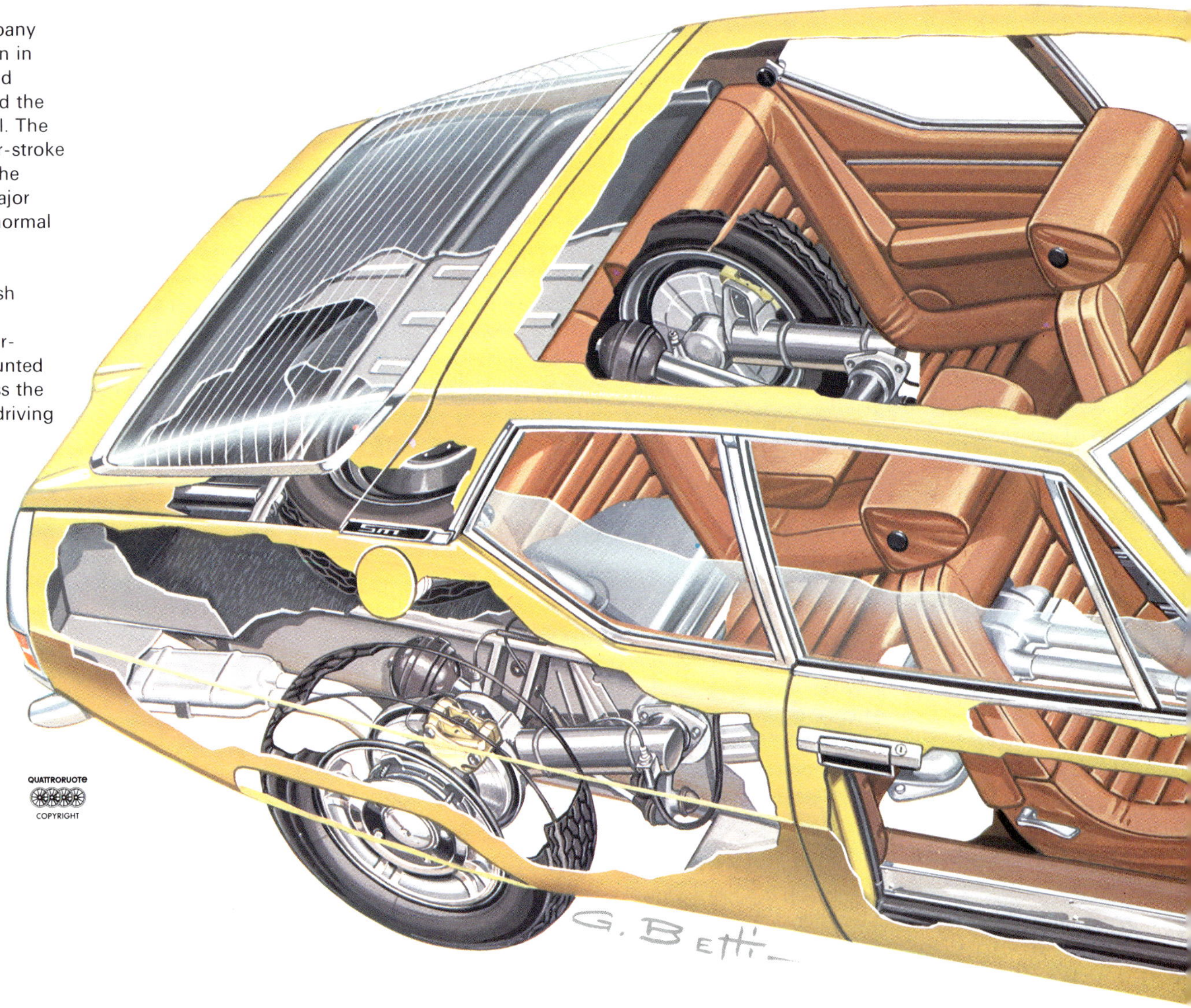

Above: once, front-wheel drive was used only for family saloons. Nowadays, however, the system has found its way onto such highly sophisticated cars as the Citroën SM. The 2.6-litre V6 engine drives the front wheels via the Citroën-designed five-speed gearbox, the car having a reputation for sure and sensitive handling

HOW IT WORKS/Front-wheel drive

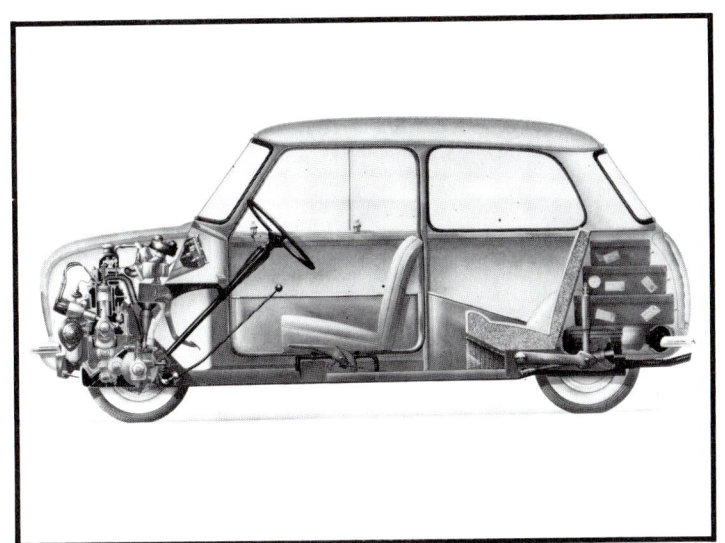

Above left: perhaps the most famous front-wheel-drive car of all time, British Leyland's ultra-successful Mini

Above right: another of the European manufacturers to employ fwd on its cars is Lancia

727

Front-wheel drive/HOW IT WORKS

Above: the start of a race at Brands Hatch and not a single rear-wheel-drive car in sight. The event was arranged especially for drivers of Renault 5 cars and this category has produced some exciting racing both in Britain and in the car's native France

type being reduced to a minimum'. Thirty years later, theorists were saying more pointedly that the front-drive car could corner faster when accelerating than when decelerating, and was inherently faster round corners than the rear-drive type when the accelerating technique was used correctly. Had they read the annals of the American Society of Automotive Engineers, they would have found that in 1926, Barney Oldfield was telling them that there was less tendency to skid provided the driver had the courage to keep his foot on the throttle: 'Just prior to the (Indianapolis) 500 Mr Duray demonstrated that, with the foot on the throttle, the car will travel in the direction in which it is pointed. Pete de Paolo demonstrated that, with the foot off the throttle, the car will not travel in the direction in which it is pointed'. Hundreds of Mini-racers would be quick to agree.

The real trouble is that it is natural and generally desirable that the preponderance of a car's weight should be over its driving wheels, and when the front wheels are driven by a frontal engine it is unavoidable that this should be so. It may give poor acceleration off the starting line or up a steep hill from standstill, because the weight transference to the rear wheels during acceleration unloads the driving wheels and permits them to spin; but these are problems that seldom beset the ordinary motorist. The problems of navigation that he encounters when naturally if cravenly releasing the accelerator during the early stages of a corner that seems too hectic are of much greater moment. While the throttle was open and the engine was delivering tractive torque to the front wheels, the tyres on those wheels would have their cornering power (already reduced by the weight they carried) further depleted by the torque they transmitted. Relieved of this torque, they would then adopt a smaller slip angle and the existing understeer would be reduced or even completely nullified, to be replaced by some degree of oversteer.

The cure that became available as the 1960s progressed was simply bigger and better tyres. Instead of working beyond the peak of the cornering force relationship—when an increase in load would decrease the tyre's cornering power—they could now operate on the upward slope of the curve: in other words, an increase in load would increase cornering power. The side effects of tractive torque would then be proportionally less, while current improvements in the sidewall construction of the now fashionable radial-ply tyres combined with wider wheel rims to reduce lateral compliance—the sideways distortion that varied sharply with changes in stress in earlier tyres. Add to this a great deal of work on the cultivation of roll steer by careful attention to suspension geometry, and the result is that today many front-wheel-drive cars are almost entirely free from the basic handling problems that beset earlier examples.

There remain some difficulties. A front-drive car has, as already noted, its centre of gravity well forward. With the driver aboard, the situation is little different; but when the driver is joined by three or four passengers, and the luggage boot is fully laden, and the fuel tank (usually in the tail of the car) is full, then the centre of gravity moves a long way towards the rear. In a car as substantial and long and relatively low as, say, the Citroën DS, the effect may not be very noticeable—and in that particular car it is further masked by self-levelling suspension. But it is in the small car that front-wheel drive has proved to offer the strongest commercial attractions, and in a small car the migration of the centre of gravity can have serious consequences. The cornering balance obviously suffers; so does the braking balance, for if the distribution of braking effort is arranged so as to prevent premature locking of the rear wheels when the car is running light, braking efficiency will be impaired in the fully laden state. The same weight shift will make steep hill starts difficult, and play havoc with the alignment of the headlamp beams. A front-engined rear-driven car generally displays less sensitivity to load because it is more evenly balanced, while a tail-heavy rear-engined four-seater is least affected of all, the rear-seat passengers coming between the engine and the driver and sitting roughly coincident with the centre of gravity.

For many years it was held that the rear-engined car was the cheapest to make, because it dispensed with the propeller shaft and it did not demand complex transmission elements as did the front-drive car. The introduction of the Rzeppa ball-type constant-velocity universal joint, and the adoption of the transverse engine configuration in the BMC Mini, overcame these objections. It was the Mini which set new standards for the ratio of habitable to total volumes and thus made the really small car truly practical. As in the case of the Light 15 Citroën, its wide track, low build, and natural disposition of a wheel at each corner endowed it with roadholding and agility that also set new standards; and since that time there has been a steady proselytizing among car designers so that more and more of the world's small cars are driven by their front wheels. It was perhaps a *jeu d'ésprit* by the General Motors marketing men, rather than a sense of *noblesse oblige* in their engineers, that saw to it that one of the world's biggest cars, the Oldsmobile Toronado, should also be thus contrived. Since it too was surprisingly well-behaved, it may be concluded that front-wheel drive must have its virtues; and on icy roads there is no doubting them. Only when the power:weight ratio reaches super-sporting levels do the vices begin to predominate. LJKS

THE MOTOR INDUSTRY/Frua

NEW BODIES FOR OLD

Italian coachbuilders have long been famous for their exciting, graceful and sophisticated designs. Typical of these is Pietro Frua

ALTHOUGH THE STYLING WORKSHOP of Pietro Frua is less well known than those of Bertone and Pininfarina the company has remained in business since 1944, during which period many more famous names have either been taken over or gone out of business.

Before World War II, Pietro Frua worked for several of the larger styling studios in Italy, including a ten-year spell with Stablimenti Farina, which ended just before the war in 1937. After hostilities ceased in 1945, Frua decided to set up in business on his own, taking a studio in Turin. As well as the more glamorous car-styling exercises he also took on a good deal of industrial work which was more lucrative.

His earlier efforts in the automobile field centred on small cars like the Fiat 1100TV cabriolet, Peugeot 203 coupé, Renault Dauphine and the Fiat 600, on which he built a coupé body. In 1955 he was called in, along with several other stylists, to design bodies for the A6G2000 Maserati. This was a roadgoing version of the 2-litre racing car which had been quite successful in international events. He also rebodied an Osca sports car and designed the body for the 1956 Nardi sports car which sold moderately well in the USA, after being exhibited at the New York Show.

Frua's big breakthrough into designing bodies for major manufacturers came when Renault asked him to design a new sports body for their improved Dauphine chassis. The result was the Renault Floride, still regarded by many as one of the most attractive two door bodies ever designed for a small car. He followed up with the Caravelle which was a convertible version that later also became available as a coupé. These models continued in production for over six years.

Beauty, grace and imagination are hallmarks of Frua designs. Using the mechanicals of the Opel Diplomat, Frua created two highly individual machines. Pictured above is the sleek sports coupé, while the dignified saloon version appears on the right

This page, top to bottom: one of Frua's earliest designs, a Fiat 1100 saloon;

Frua's Maserati 2000 A6GCS Gransport design;

a convertible 'one-off', based on the Fiat 1100;

the superbly balanced Maserati Quatroporte of 1963

Opposite page, top: first shown in 1963, the Maserati Mistrale is regarded as one of the world's classic body designs

Centre left: a racy-looking Maserati 2-litre Sport of 1956

Centre right: Frua has done much work for the Maserati company. This is the 2000 GT Spider model of 1957

Bottom: the 1965 Maserati Mistrale convertible. The car was powered by a 3.7-litre, 285 bhp motor and had a top speed of 155 mph

Frua also designed the body for the ill-fated German-built Lloyd 600 and in 1959 he designed the standard body for the Maserati 3500 GT. This was to lead to much more work from Maserati, who commissioned him to design the 5000 GT coupé, followed by the four-door Quatroporte saloon and the Mistrale coupé All these cars were built in series production by Maserati for several years. The Mistrale is regarded as one of the world's classic body designs and its shape has been reflected in several other Frua designs.

One-off jobs continued to take a good deal of Frua's time and he produced such cars as a Volkswagen coupé, a big saloon on a Studebaker Lark chassis, and a pretty coupé body in steel on the Lotus Elan at the 1964 Geneva Motor Show. This car was commissioned by the Swiss Lotus concessionaire and although reputedly going into production never made it.

In 1963, Frua reached an agreement with the German company of Hans Glas, under which he was to design all their range of production cars. Several handsome cars resulted, including the 1700 GT coupé, the 2600 V8, the 1304 TS saloon and the 1700 limousine. These cars did much to improve the image of the company, which had started out building the tiny Goggomobil, but the firm got into financial difficulties and was eventually taken over by BMW. BMW planned to keep the 1700 GT going by grafting on their own independent suspension in place of the Glas live axle, but the car never went into serious production.

Frua's liaison with Glas led to a few styling jobs with Opel, for whom he designed an open version of the Kadett which was shown at the Frankfurt Show. He also designed a convertible Maserati, which went into production as the 3500 GTI.

In 1965, Britain's AC car company were looking for a new body to replace the American-designed Cobra

THE MOTOR INDUSTRY/Frua

Left: in 1964, Frua exhibited his version of the Lotus Elan at the Geneva Motor Show

Below: one of the best known of all Frua designs is the Renault Floride. The car was based on Renault's Dauphine model and soon became a best seller around the world. This is the convertible version

two-seater and their Swiss agent suggested that Frua be given the job of designing a new body. He came up with a convertible, not unlike his Maserati shapes, and AC decided to go into production with this model on a lengthened AC Cobra chassis. This was named the AC 428 convertible. In 1967, Frua designed a coupé body for the AC 428, this model resembling his Maserati Mistrale coupé in many details. As well as designing the bodies, Frua also built them in steel on chassis which were shipped out to him in Turin. He continued building the AC 428 bodies in small quantities until 1973, when the model was finally dropped.

When Peter Monteverdi was planning to enter motor manufacturing again in 1968, he commissioned Frua to design and build the bodies for his large Chrysler-powered saloons and coupés, but Frua lost this contract to Fissore.

Since 1968, Frua has largely been concerned with one-off projects for individual owners and design exercises intended to persuade manufacturers to take up the design. Few commissions, however, have come his way in recent years, largely because younger designers like Guigiaro have come into vogue with new shapes and new ideas.

However, Frua has built one-off bodies on a Chevrolet Camaro, a BMW 2000 TI, an Opel Diplomat and a BMW 2800. In 1971 he built a special-bodied Porsche 914/6, a 5-litre V8 Maserati and a revised version of his Glas coupé using Ford 1600 components. He also designed a body for an American, Alfred Momo, who was planning to build a series of cars, but this never materialised.

One successful car that Frua did build was the Ligier JS1, designed by French racing driver Guy Ligier. This car was initially powered by a Cosworth-Ford engine and later by the V6 Citroën-Maserati engine and gearbox. Frua designed the body for this dual-purpose road/racing coupé and had it built in glass fibre. The later Ligier JS2 was quite successful in racing, being a regular runner at Le Mans, but it was not put into serious production.

Frua moved from his old workshops to Moncalieri where he continued to build one-offs for special customers. Recent customers have been the Shah of Persia and the Aga Khan. Frua's latest show car is a vast body on a Rolls-Royce Phantom VI chassis. The pea-green convertible was built for a Swiss Rolls-Royce enthusiast who wanted something different from the usual Phantom VI Limousine shape. MT

Opposite page: clockwise:
the 1963 Glas 1300GT;

the Rolls Royce Phantom V1, presented at the 1973 Frankfurt Motor Show, is the only one of its kind;

the prototype version of Frua's AC 428 successor;

the final production version of the AC 428. As well as designing the car, Frua also built it in steel on chassis shipped out to him in Turin

Fuel/HOW IT WORKS

LIFE BLOOD OF THE MOTOR CAR

Just about all motor vehicles take their fuel from crude oil. Even electric cars rely largely on oil-fired power stations

Above: a view of Oil Island, in the Persian Gulf, which is the heart of the oil empire

Right: the chart shows how the specific gravities of the fractions from the various crude oils of the world vary. As far as gasoline is concerned, that from the naphthenic oils has a higher octane than that from the waxy paraffinic oils

PETROLEUM IS A HYDROCARBON, a compound of carbon and hydrogen only. The 'petrol' you buy from a pump may also contain lead-tetra-ethyl, ethyl dibromide, halowax oil, xylidine, tricresylphosphate, catechol, and various other additives whose presence or absence may depend on the octane rating of the product, the country where it is sold, or the time of year. Even the basic crude oil from which it is derived, will vary in characteristics according to its place of origin: the stuff from the East Indies is very different from Californian, which is again very different from what is found in the eastern states of the USA.

Of course, there are other fuels that have been or are used for propelling cars, but their cases are little less confusing. Benzol, benzene, or C_6H_6 (from which you may properly deduce that it is another hydrocarbon), comes from coal tar and coal gas. The stuff you buy commercially is known as 90% benzol, but the world of commerce being what it is, the benzol content is actually 81%. It served as the regular fuel of high-performance engines until the chemists got around to giving us high-octane gasoline.

Or shall be try alcohol, once the standby of the racing man? Ethyl alcohol, C_2H_5OH, is produced by fermentation of any carbohydrate such as that from grain or potatoes. Not the best alcohol for motor fuel, it has the saving grace of being potable, but whisky distillers and the like have to be careful not to carry distillation too far lest methanol result, which is bad for reputation and customers alike. Methanol is methyl alcohol, CH_3OH, and if drunk will make you blind, mad and dead in that order. Since it can be produced by the destructive distillation of wood, it is sometimes called wood alcohol and its properties make it splendid as a fuel for high-compression or (especially) supercharged engines of high specific output. Yet, when methanol is supplied as a racing fuel, it is usually impure: acetone has to be added to cure pre-ignition.

Looking back at the formula for these alcohols, it may be noted that as well as carbon and hydrogen, they also contain oxygen. So, in even richer proportions, do all the 'nitro' fuels fed to the most rabidly powerful sprinting engines. Nitrous oxide, for example, employed as a temporary vitaliser in certain selected Spitfire fighters late in World War II, is, in its liquid form, one-third oxygen by volume. It and the other nitro fuels—nitro-methane, and the like—are chemically related to nitric acid. Despite being one of the most corrosive agents going, the acid is used raw in some modern rocket engines, combining with kerosene to burn with terrific intensity at temperatures which would melt a piston engine.

Whatever the chosen fuel, and however it may burn, it does so by combining with oxygen; and this is why the superfuels carry some oxygen with them, in a more concentrated form than can be found in the ambient nitrogen-diluted atmosphere. Oxygen has an almost sexual proclivity for joining with practically everything that happens to be in the vicinity, for the basic atom of oxygen is short of a couple of electrons, which makes it as ravenous as a stud bull. It may react with hydrogen to form water, or with iron to form rust. That alcohol in the racer's tank—there is an atom of oxygen locked in the embrace of each alcoholic molecule. If, as is likely, the alcohol is laced with ether, there will be an oxygen atom to be found embosomed between carbon in each ethereal molecule.

To check this orgiastic behaviour, special extinguishers are needed for dealing with fuel fires. Most of them rely on blanketing the flames with a gas that will not support combustion, for water will only spread the fire and make it worse. Carbon tetrachloride (CTC) was once the accepted extinguishant; but when used, it liberates a gas which is converted to the deadly phosgene if inhaled through a cigarette.

Petrol and all the other fuels are essentially dangerous commodities, only too ready to succumb to the advances of the oxygen in the air. Even worse than the petrol fire is the petrol explosion, caused when a certain mixture of air and fuel is ignited in a closed container such as a car, a petrol tank, or a garage. It seems part of the very contrary nature of petrol that almost any proportion of it with air will serve to blow a garage to smithereens, but only a carefully controlled mixture between 1:8 and 1:18 is likely to ignite inside an engine that was built for it.

When it does ignite, it may burn or explode according to how well matched it is to the engine's needs. Petrol too low in octane value will show signs of detonation, bad for performance and bad for the engine itself. 'Octane value' is a common expression which ought to be replaced by anti-knock value, for this is what the octane scale measures: the higher the figure, the higher the resistance to knock or detonation. Octane is simply one of the series of light distillates produced from crude oil, and gets its name from the eight carbon atoms in each molecule. Heptane (seven carbon atoms) is another, and has a pronounced tendency to cause knocking, whereas octane at one time had the highest resistance of all fuels used or known. So a petrol of 87 octane rating was equivalent in it knock resistance to a mixture of 87% octane and 13% heptane. This was a satisfactory measure until the chemists introduced fuels whose octane rating suggested a mixture of more than 100% octane and presumably a negative percentage of heptane. This was nonsensical, but fuels of such high ratings could be produced, and the demands of military aviation saw to it that they were. Already it was known that petrols with a high aromatic content had a higher anti-knock value than those which had not. Soon, the American Thomas Midgley, in his studies of knock, hit upon the use of aromatic amines such as xylidine as detonation suppressants. Then, in about 1922, he discovered the effects of tetraethyl lead (TEL), and petrol has never been the same since.

HOW IT WORKS/Fuel

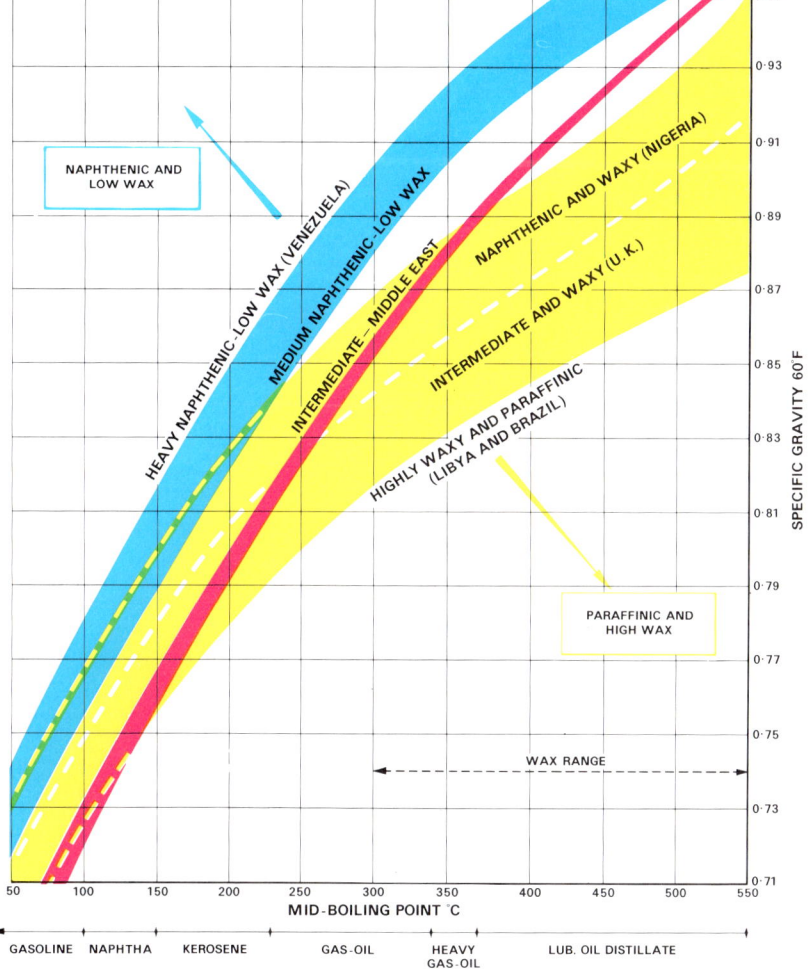

TEL had its drawbacks. Lead oxides formed on the combustion chamber and exhaust valves, lead salts (electrically conductive) on spark plug insulators. Ethyl dibromide fluid dealt with the deposits, halowax oil served to lubricate the valve stems. Still, it took time for TEL to catch on, for there was no reliable means of testing the anti-knock rating of fuels —until in 1927 another American, Graham Edgar, discovered iso-octane, which he combined with normal heptane to establish the octane number scale that we now all use, know, and to some extent understand.

In fact, there are two scales. One measures knock resistance at very low speeds when the engine is really 'lugging', and is known as the Research Method. The other applies to higher speeds and is the Motor Method, and its figures are somewhat lower. The difference between the two is called the sensitivity number: about 5 or 6 for the best grades of pump petrol, it is becoming more important as social pressures act, to reduce the anti-knock properties of premium petrols in the hope of reducing emissions of lead and of oxides of nitrogen. The use of the more volatile tetramethyl lead (TML) instead of TEL was a palliative, but there are people who want to be entirely rid of the stuff.

Leadless petrol of high anti-knock value can be made. During World War II, enthusiasm ran high for a new superfuel called triptane, having much of the character of conventional gasolines but so resistant to detonation that an engine designed to exploit it could, in theory, develop three times as much power as one doing its best with 100 RON (Research Octane Number) fuel. Everyone thought triptane would win the war for the Allies until it was calculated that to produce it in sufficient quantities would consume the entire chlorine output of the USA! Today, it can be made: existing alkyation processes are used to make a number of high-octane quality blending agents, and triptane (2,2,3 trimethylbutane, should you be interested) is one that can be used to restore the properties of premium pump fuels derived of their lead compounds.

Clearly it is in knock resistance that the secret of power lies. Unfortunately, the octane rating scales do not give a clear measure of this potential, and fuel chemists sometimes prefer a scale of performance numbers (PN) which offer a roughly linear rating corresponding to the power output they make possible. PN and RON scales coincide at 100; but a 72 RON fuel would have a PN of 50, indicating that an engine using it would be limited to half the power output of an engine fully adapted to 100 PN fuel. The figures we used to encounter, late in the war years, referring to aviation gasolines of 100/130, 100/150, or 115/145 grades, were performance numbers. But why two? Because it had been discovered (by the British Air Ministry in the late 1930s) that different gasolines, equally resistant to detonation in lean-mixture operation, might be very different in their behaviours during take-off or combat emergency conditions involving rich mixture. Studying the range of PN ratings over the years, we can see that improvements in gasoline are responsible for a far greater proportion of the improvements in engine power since the pioneering days than anything else—in fact, a greater proportion than all other developments put together. PN ratings rose by 416% in the thirty years ending in 1945—making it ironic that for some years afterwards, the quality of motor fuels was execrable, only reaching 90 plus RON ratings in 1953. Today, the best pump gasolines rate 100–101 RON and 95 MON.

However, there remain many other factors to

Fuel

This diagram shows the basic components of a fractionating column used for the breakdown of crude oil. The petroleum is heated and fed into the main column, where steam keeps it at the correct temperature for the lighter fractions to boil off. The temperature drops as the vapour rises up the tower and the various distillates collect in special trays situated about two feet apart. The heaviest fraction, the residue, is taken to a storage tank after transferring some of its heat to fresh crude oil. The lightest fraction is taken from the column as vapour and is condensed by cooling water. Each fraction is further purified in small columns known as strippers, the lighter 'cuts' being fed back into the main column

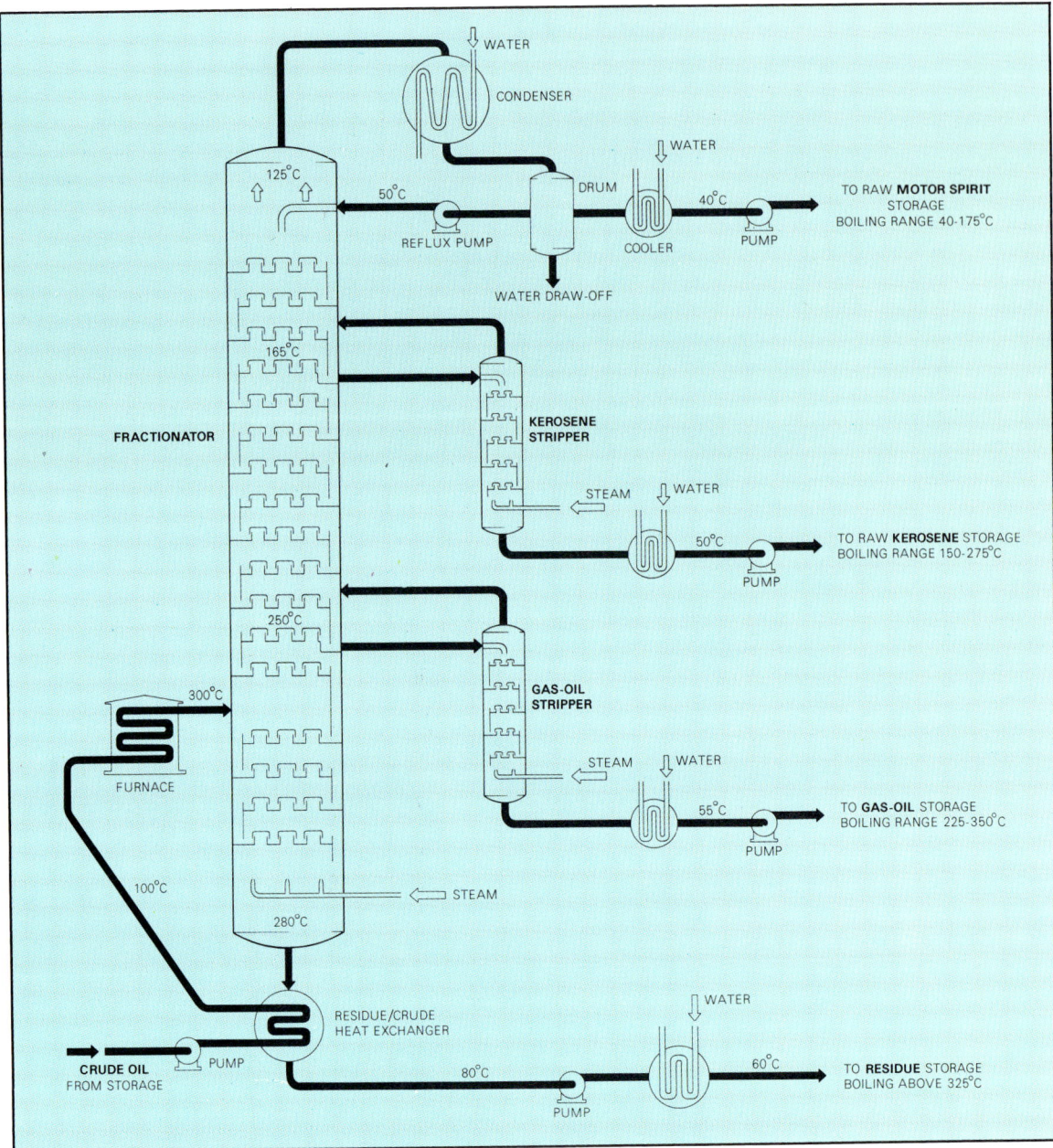

consider. The stuff must remain liquid in the dead of winter (which is more than benzole would unless treated with additives), so a little toluene or xylene must be added. Ice formation inside the carburettor is another problem, overcome to a large extent by the addition of isopropyl alcohol. To ensure ready starting at low temperatures, high volatility is essential: in winter, the oil companies take care to include particularly 'light' distillates produced in the fractionating columns of refineries where crude oil is broken down into a variety of products including paraffins, lubricating oils, diesel oils and tars, *et cetera*. Too much volatility causes vapour lock and leads to losses by evaporation in hot weather, whenever the recipe is adjusted accordingly.

What of the racing fuels, the alcohols and so forth? They are little used now, simply because the oil companies refused to support racing unless it served to advertise their normal gasolines. This decision, which became effective in the highest forms of racing at the end of 1957, had three effects: it encouraged combustion studies, increased fire risks, and virtually outlawed the supercharger. This was because alcohol fuels are very insensitive to mixture strength, very resistant to knock, and have a tremendous cooling effect which is essential in a pressure-charged engine of competitive performance, while burning slowly.

When racing cars used alcohol, their fuel consumption was enormous: the supercharged, 1½-litre Alfa Romeo of 1950 did about 1½ miles per gallon. This was because alcohol has a low calorific content: the amount of chemical energy in it that can be converted to heat energy in an engine is only about half that of the same weight of gasoline, which means that alcohol is not a very efficient power source.

Outside racing, other natural fuels have been considered from time to time. Most popular are the liquified petroleum gases such as butane, propane and methane. The last named is much the best: its calorific value is high, it allows very high compression ratios (and hence high power) because of its high knock resistance, it does not dilute or destroy the lubricating oil films within the engine (a particularly bad habit of alcohols, some of which react badly to certain oil additives), and it is cheap to manufacture as a by-product of sewage. It could well be one of the fuels of the future, but already engineers are talking with some conviction of the probability of simple hydrogen being the normal fuel for internal combustion engines (possibly of continuous-combustion type) by the end of the century. Hydrogen may be produced by the electrolysis of water or in nuclear power stations, and this would cause no ecological upheaval. As a simple gas or liquid, it would be awkward to store and handle, but in some combined form such as ammonia, hydrazine or a metal hydride it has possibilities. LJKS

HOW IT WORKS/Fuel gauge

A MEASURE OF CONSUMPTION

The fuel gauge is one of the motor car's more vital instruments. There is nothing more annoying than running out of fuel because of a faulty or inaccurate gauge

THE FUEL GAUGE OF A MODERN CAR comprises two main parts—the familiar dial indicator on the dash panel and a unit hidden away in the petrol tank which is responsible for 'measuring' the fuel in the tank.

The latter is a circular unit, mounted in a circular hole in the tank and bolted in position, the joint being sealed with a rubber gasket. Sticking out of the unit into the tank is an arm and on the end of the arm is a float assembly.

When the unit is bolted in place and petrol is put into the tank, the float rests on the surface. As the fuel level rises, the end of the arm inside the tank unit sweeps a small 'finger' across a variable resistance. Electrical current from the battery is passed through the dial to the tank unit and part of the resistance, depending where the arm is positioned at the time. The circuit is completed via earth.

The amount of resistance that is in circuit at any time affects the current supplied to the dial and this, in turn, affects the position of the needle on the dial. In principle, the dial mechanism consists of a length of resistance wire wound round a bimetalic strip. As current passes, the wire heats the strip which, due to the different expansion rates of the two metals, bends and moves the gauge needle.

Basically, the sequence is, the higher the level of petrol, the lower the resistance in the tank unit. This means a higher current and an increased reading at the petrol gauge end.

Total accuracy is seldom found in any petrol gauge unless it has been individually calibrated. It is a good idea for the owner to experiment every time he acquires a new vehicle. Note when the needle registers EMPTY and then count how many more miles the car will travel before it runs out completely. Some gauges say EMPTY and mean it; others might have two or three gallons still in the tank. A little time spent investigating petrol gauge irregularities initially may save a lot of time at a later stage.

When things go wrong

Usually, if there is a fault in the fuel gauge circuit, it shows up because the needle continuously registers EMPTY even though the petrol tank may be full. There are a number of possible faults.

Before you start checking, it is always a good idea to disconnect the battery. Start your investigation with all the wiring connections. Ensure that the gauge is properly earthed. This is particularly important when the instrument panel is not a metal one. There will be a separate earth wire which must make good contact at both ends. The power input wire must also be sound and properly connected at both ends. Both of these are usually well protected behind the dash panel but could be disconnected.

If the fault is in the wire connecting gauge and tank unit, it will be because the wire has been hit or sqaushed

in some way and is short circuited directly to earth.

If the fault does not appear to be in the wiring, it could be that the gauge itself is faulty. This can be checked by disconnecting the wire which goes to the tank at the gauge end. Reconnecting the battery and turning on the ignition should result in the gauge reading FULL. If the tank terminal on the gauge is not connected directly to earth, the needle should swing right across to EMPTY. If this happens, the gauge is sound and working properly and there is obviously no need for further investigation.

If you suspect the tank unit is faulty, you can check it. For obvious reasons, try to ensure that the petrol level in the tank is below the position of the tank unit and then take out the tank unit—it is only a matter of removing a single wiring connection and some screws. The battery will, of course, already have been disconnected, in order to minimise any risk of a short circuit and resultant fire.

Check first that the arm is moving freely. Then, by re-connecting the wire to the gauge and the battery, switching on the ignition and earthing the tank unit body, check that moving the arm results in the gauge needle moving. If the needle shows FULL only, either the tank unit is defective, or there is a faulty connection or a break in the tank-unit-to-dashboard-gauge wiring. In this case, the wiring must be traced and all connections checked.
JJ

All car fuel gauges are electrically operated. The float, *above left*, which measures the level of fuel in the tank, operates a variable resistance. The resistance, *above right*, alters the amount of electricity being supplied to the meter or gauge

Fuel injection/HOW IT WORKS

AN ALTERNATIVE TO THE CARBURETTOR

The requirements of emission-control regulations have affected the carburettor severely, thus bringing the fuel-injection principle into the position of a practical alternative

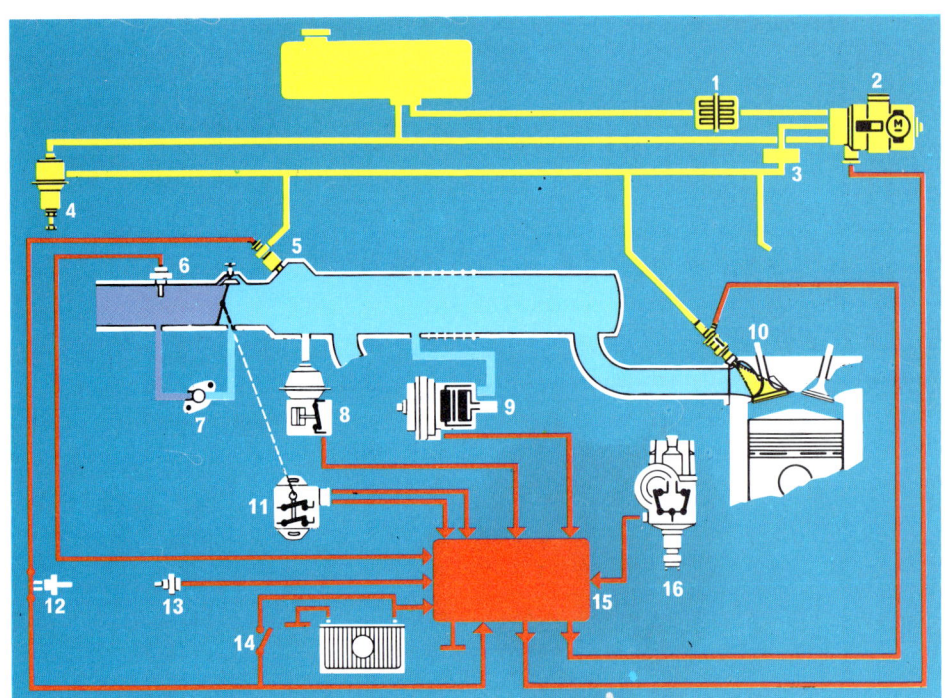

A diagrammatic representation of an electronic indirect fuel-injection system, showing the layout of the components:
1 fuel filter
2 electric pump
3 damper
4 pressure regulator
5 cold-starting injector
6 air-intake-temperature sensor
7 supplementary-air valve
8 pressure switch
9 pressure sensor
10 injector
11 throttle switch
12 thermal switch
13 temperature sensor
14 ignition switch
15 electronic control centre
16 breakerless distributor

BY SQUIRTING MEASURED DOSES of fuel into the inlet manifold, inlet ports, or even into the cylinders themselves, fuel injection apparatus gives an engine what it should have; a carburettor, from which fuel is sucked by the flow of intake air, allows it to take what it wants. Since neither system has yet been made perfect, neither achieves these ideals, but social pressures on technology have, in recent years, been responsible for a considerable improvement in both, and in particular for a readier acceptance of the idea that injection might supplant the carburettor in ordinary cars as it long ago did in racing cars.

It would be a mistake to suppose that the success of injection in racing proved that it gave more power. It does not necessarily do so: the only reason for the superior power of most injected engines is that the venturi, or restricted throat, of most carburettors (necessary to promote the pressure drop that sucks fuel from the jet) imposes a limit on the air-breathing ability of the engine, and it is the rate of air intake that determines the power output. There are, however, carburettors that allow as free an airflow as the best injection systems—the Amal GP, long used on racing motor cycles, is a good example—and when one of these is used for each cylinder, the power realised need be no less than when injection is applied to individual inlet tracts as in current racing engines. Racing engines tend to have a large number of cylinders, however, and the weight and complexity of a corresponding number of carburettors (each of which must be adjusted individually to some extent, even in the most ingenious multiple mountings) then constitute severe disadvantages; the centralised control and delivery systems of injection apparatus are by comparison lighter, more compact and easier to adjust. More severe still in racing is the carburettor's sensitivity to surge of fuel in the float chamber as the car corners hard or brakes heavily: the best Grand Prix cars corner at as much as $1.7g$, when the fuel inside a carburettor would be flung to one side so forcefully that its surface would adopt an angle 59 degrees away from the horizontal—with what ensuing difficulties in starving or flooding the jets may be imagined.

The ordinary roadgoing car does not have a lot of cylinders and does not corner with such ferocity. What advantages then remain to justify the adoption of injection? In theory, there are at least ten:
1 because of the absence of venturi restrictions which ordinary carburettors cannot avoid, volumetric (or breathing) efficiency is higher, and so therefore should be the power output;
2 mixture distribution is better, each cylinder being given the same dosage;
3 mixture strength is uniform for each cylinder;
4 fuel economy is better because of 2 and 3;

HOW IT WORKS/Fuel injection

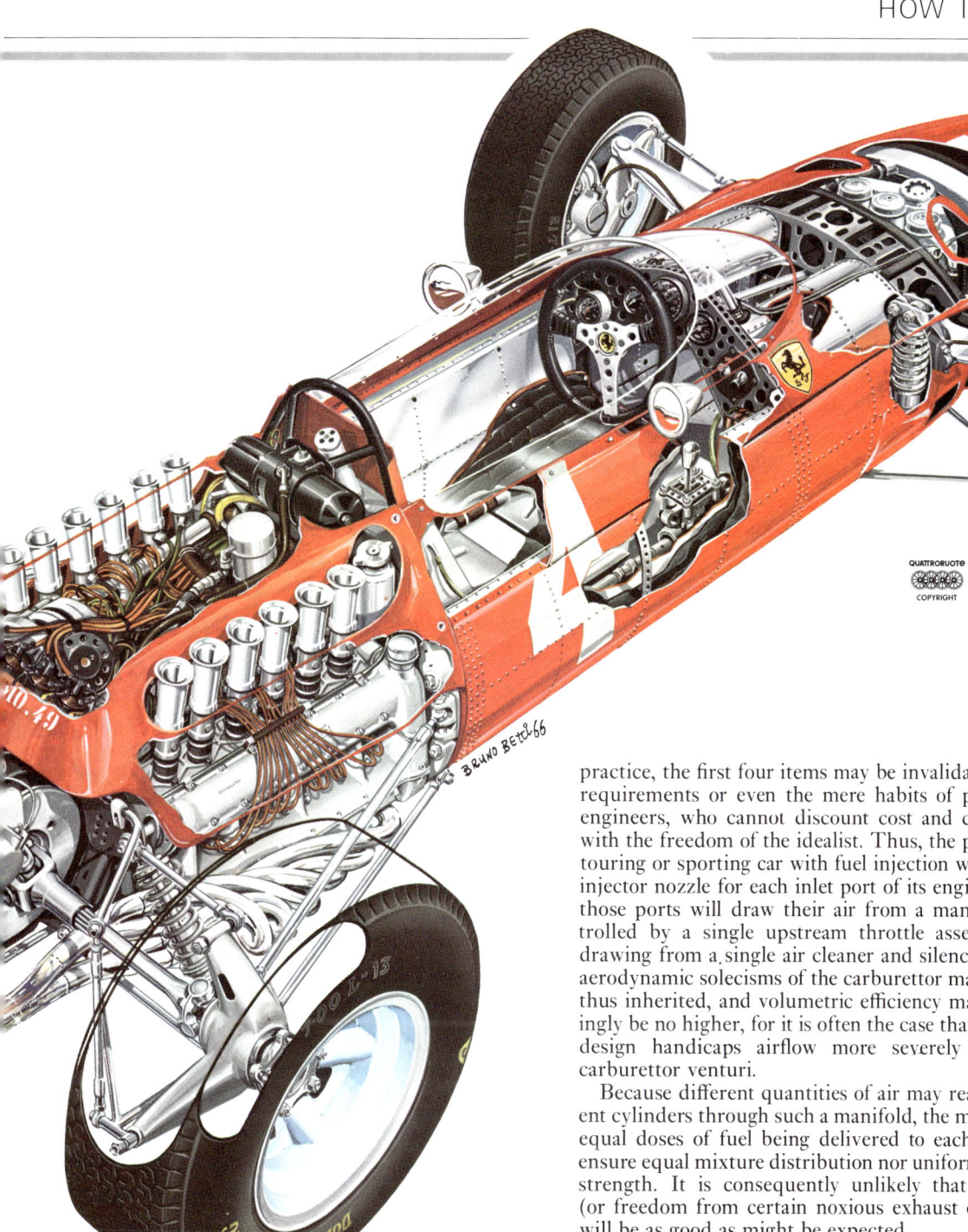

The Ferrari 1512 Formula One car of 1965. Its flat-twelve, 1489 cc engine used fuel injection, as do all Formula One cars. Racing is the most popular application for fuel injection, other than diesel engines, although many manufacturers have at least experimented with injection for road cars

5 there is mechanically induced reduction of the liquid fuel to fine droplets, hence no need to heat the inlet air to ensure adequate vaporisation, and therefore no loss of volumetric efficiency due to the lower density of heated air;

6 acceleration response is better, the extra fuel needed being injected forthwith instead of flowing only after air flow has changed and depression has drawn it from the jets;

7 cold starting is better because of 5 and 6;
8 idling is more uniform because of 2 and 3;
9 inlet-valve cooling is improved, because latent heat of evaporation need not be taken out of the fuel earlier in its passage (this is not valid in the case of direct injection into the cylinder);

10 icing in very cold weather is absent, because of the same reason as in 9.

It is an impressive list, but it is a theoretical one. In practice, the first four items may be invalidated by the requirements or even the mere habits of production engineers, who cannot discount cost and complexity with the freedom of the idealist. Thus, the production touring or sporting car with fuel injection will have an injector nozzle for each inlet port of its engine, but all those ports will draw their air from a manifold controlled by a single upstream throttle assembly and drawing from a single air cleaner and silencer. All the aerodynamic solecisms of the carburettor manifold are thus inherited, and volumetric efficiency may accordingly be no higher, for it is often the case that manifold design handicaps airflow more severely than the carburettor venturi.

Because different quantities of air may reach different cylinders through such a manifold, the mere fact of equal doses of fuel being delivered to each does not ensure equal mixture distribution nor uniform mixture strength. It is consequently unlikely that economy (or freedom from certain noxious exhaust emissions) will be as good as might be expected.

On the other hand, if each intake port be furnished not only with its own injector but also with its own inlet pipe, throttle and air filter, results may be achieved that should be superior to any but the very best multi-carburettor arrangements, with advantages in cost, weight, accessibility, and ease of maintenance.

All this presupposes the ability to determine how much fuel should be injected, and when. Until very recently indeed, the history of fuel injection has been a confusion of blind alleys and wild geese that made this supposedly straightforward determination more like an exercise in roundabout assumptions; and the history is a long one, dating back at least to 1903 when the Wright brothers' first sustained powered flight was propelled by an engine with petrol injection—if not to the nineteenth-century origins of the diesel engine. For a long time it was oil-engine practice that was followed in experiments with petrol injection, most successfully by Bosch and Daimler-Benz in the development of fully aerobatic aero engines for the Luftwaffe; and a Bosch jerk-pump system was evolved for the BMW 328 sports cars specially built

Fuel injection/HOW IT WORKS

Chevrolet's Cosworth Vega engine. The main differences between this and the ordinary Vega unit are that this has twin overhead cams and fuel injection. The injection tubes can be seen, one on each induction pipe. The intakes are linked at their open ends so that only one throttle is necessary (*top*)

for the 1940 Mille Miglia race, though it was not in fact used.

The jerk pump contains a number of plungers moved by a camshaft geared to the engine speed, each plunger displacing fuel from its cylinder through small-bore piping to an injector nozzle feeding an inlet port or engine cylinder. A rotating rack and quadrant mechanism turns the plungers in their bores so as to vary the unmasking of plunger-controlled ports which, in turn, govern the quantity of fuel transmitted on each stroke; this mechanism is linked to the throttle pedal and to a pneumatic sensor of inlet manifold vacuum, so as to cater for variations in engine demand. It was an imperfect system when applied to the petrol engine, but for racing machines exploiting alcohol-based fuels that were not sensitive to mixture strength, it worked well enough, and the 1954/55 Mercedes-Benz Grand Prix cars introduced it most effectively to racing. Already, there had been other attempts, also reliant on the forgiving nature of alcohol fuels: the Hilborn continuous injection system, in which the only variation in supply was by varying the pressure of fuel pumped to the injector nozzles in the ports, was much favoured at Indianapolis and was tried successfully in England by Connaught in their 1953 Formula Two car. Vanwall went to Bosch for help with their Grand Prix car, and in 1958 were probably the first to run a racing car with petrol injection when other fuels were proscribed.

Nevertheless, it was the perfection by Lucas of an ingenious shuttle metering system that made possible the more popular modern approach to the problem, in which an electrically driven pump pressurises the delivery of fuel to an engine-driven distributor that puts each injector in communication with this pressure in its appropriate turn. A cam or lever moved by the accelerator pedal adjusts the abutments that stop the metering shuttle at the end of each stroke, and thus varies the quantity of fuel displaced by each movement. For racing this is sufficient, but for a road car there is once again a need for finer control, provided by a pneumatic transducer sensitive to intake manifold pressure. A similar sensor can adjust the mixture according to ambient atmospheric pressure. This Lucas system provides timed doses of fuel to each cylinder, but it was demonstrated by BRM (who were the first to employ it) that the timing was not critical. Other manufacturers of injection apparatus took advantage of this insensitivity to simplify their systems by adopting a continuous spray, the quantity of fuel delivered being varied by alterations in delivery pressure. The Tecalemit-Jackson system, capable of giving an engine as much power potential as any form of injection or carburation, was one such. In general, however, it was found that the means of sensing all the different parameters that affected the engine's need for mixture, in terms of quantity and richness, were the aspect of design that needed most development, and numerous injection systems that appeared in the 1950s and 1960s (particularly in the USA but also in Europe and Japan) left something to be desired.

The difficulties of translating things such as throttle position and manifold depression into measures of engine load, and relating the answer to engine speed and atmospheric pressure and ambient and engine temperatures (the needs of cold starting and fast idling during warm-up had to be remembered), promoted great variety in experiments. Bosch, Bendix, Lucas and others tried electronic control, arguing that it enabled any number of factors to be measured and corresponding adjustments to be made: a miniature transistorised computer sorted all these transducer signals and issued a pulse of current of a certain duration to solenoid-controlled injector nozzles supplied with fuel at constant pressure. The longer the pulse, the more petrol would be squirted into each port during each operating cycle of the engine. Other firms, such as Kügelfischer, relied on mechanical refinements, such as a three-dimensional cam controlling the fuel-distributor output.

It was perhaps unfortunate that for a long time nobody tried to make the injection apparatus measure what the carburettor measures automatically, which is the mass flow of air into the engine. In 1970, the Tecalemit engineer Jackson produced an electro-pneumatic system that actually measured what was required (instead of inferring it from other measurements), and the idea of mass-flow measurement was enthusiastically taken up thereafter by Bosch, who modified their existing electronic system accordingly. Unlike Bosch, the Tecalemit subsidiary Petrol Injection Ltd did not get their system into production; but more recently they have announced a modified version (reverting to timed injection) that is likely to find takers. As in so many of the latest developments involving injection and carburation alike, the object is now mainly to ensure the reduction of anti-social exhaust emissions in conformity with existing and anticipated legislation; a particular feature of the PI systems is the very fine atomisation of the fuel.

The requirements of emission-control regulations have affected the carburettor quite severely, making it much more complex in its most recent forms. This complexity is such as to put the carburettor and injection systems on a more even footing in terms of cost and difficulties of maintenance, matters which hitherto had been by far the most compelling of all reasons why injection should not supplant carburation. The operational simplicity of electronics now appear as positive attractions, and the usually low fuel consumption of an injected engine supports the view that the age of the glorified scent-spray may be over and the day of the little squirt about to dawn.   LJKS

HOW IT WORKS/Fuel pump

SUPPLYING THE CARBURETTOR

In order to supply the engine with essential fuel, it is necessary to mount the storage tank above the level of the carburettor—unless a fuel pump is installed, that is

An SU electric fuel pump of the type used on many popular British cars, especially from the British Leyland stable (SU is owned by BLMC). The inlet and outlet pipes are shown here—underneath them are valves and, in the case of the inlet, a filter. At the other end is a set of contact points which operate in a similar fashion to a buzzer

TO AVOID FIRE HAZARDS, the petrol tank is usually sited at the opposite end of the car from the engine. Because the tank is positioned low down under the floor on most cars, gravity feed is not a practical possibility and fuel has to be pumped from tank to carburettor. The pump used is one of two basic types—mechanically or electrically operated.

Mechanical pumps

These are always driven by means of an eccentric lobe on the camshaft. This operates the pump lever which is connected, by means of a rod, to the pump diaphragm. When the cam operates the lever, the diaphragm flexes and draws petrol into the lower chamber past a one-way valve. At the same time, more fuel is drawn into the upper chamber from the inlet pipe, passing via the sediment filter in the top of the pump housing.

As the operating lever passes onto the back of the cam, a spring reasserts the diaphragm. The petrol just drawn into the lower chamber is then pushed, via another one-way valve, through the outlet pipe to the carburettor's float chamber.

Each revolution of the camshaft repeats the process. The interesting part of the operation is that the fuel is pushed on its way by spring pressure only. Thus when the needle valve in the carburettor float chamber closes and no more fuel can flow, the diaphragm stays down, although the operating lever is still being pushed to and fro.

Because of the very simple component parts and uncomplicated action of the pump, it needs very little attention and not a great deal goes wrong with it. The main service procedure is a very simple one. It merely involves moving the top clip, lifting off the dome, taking out the small sediment filter inside, cleaning it with petrol and replacing it. If the filter becomes damaged it is possible for specks of dirt to lodge in the valves and stop them closing, so it is important to keep it clean and sound.

Air leaks are another possibility and these usually occur because of damage to the sealing gasket under the rim of the dome cover. This is usually made of cork and it is as well to check it and fit a new one from time to time. The top dome, incidentally, is either made of glass or metal and may be secured with a single screw instead of a wire clip.

The makers of the AC pump—one of the most common—market an overhaul kit, comprising a new diaphragm, two new one-way valves, a new top gasket and assorted other gaskets. It is not an expensive item to buy and, once installed, will completely refurbish your pump.

You will need to take the pump off the engine to overhaul it and this is usually a matter of two nuts (if the pump is mounted on studs), or perhaps two bolts. The inlet and outlet pipes must be disconnected, too.

Fuel pump/HOW IT WORKS

An AC-Delco mechanically operated fuel pump with the glass bowl and filter removed. The actuating lever *(right)* moves the diaphragm (pink edge can be seen) up and down; this, with the help of two valves feeds the carburettors

Before dismantling, mark the two flanges of the pump, so they can be put back in the same place. Note the position of the two one-way valves before taking them out as this will help to get the new ones assembled correctly. Fitting the new diaphragm has its complications. With the mounting flange of the pump in a 12 o'clock position, fit the diaphragm with its locating tab at 11 o'clock, engage the notch in the pull rod and turn around to 8 o'clock. Finally, when reassembling the two halves, finger tighten all the screws, then pull the operating arm towards the pump and hold it there while tightening.

Electric pumps

This type works in much the same basic way as the mechanical type. Movement of a diaphragm sucks in petrol in one direction and pushes it towards the carburettor when flexed the other way. The difference is that the operating rod is moved by a solenoid which is controlled by a set of contact-breaker points.

What happens is that spring pressure on the diaphragm pushes fuel out through the outlet pipe towards the carburettor. The diaphragm is connected to the rocker mechanism attached to the points and the movement closes the points. Current flows and energises the solenoid attracting the armature which is attached to the diaphragm. This is pulled towards the solenoid, drawing in fuel as it moves. Movement continues in this direction until the rocker mechanism throws over again and the points are opened. Then the spring behind the diaphragm takes over again and reverses the direction of the movement, pumping the fuel out.

Somewhat more complicated than the mechanical type, the electric pump is nevertheless still remarkably trouble free. A filter protects the pump against dirt in the petrol. This needs taking out and cleaning every 6000 miles. It is reached by undoing a hexagon plug in the base of the body—the filter is a gauze tube behind it. Some of the other types of electric pump will have to be taken off the car and the filter reached by dismantling from the bottom end. The service technique is a simple one of washing the filter in petrol and then replacing it.

If the pump stops operating altogether, disconnect the electric feed wire from its terminal. With the ignition switched on and the terminal well away from the pump, attempt to create a spark by gently brushing the wire against the car chassis. If there is no spark you will have to track the wire further back, looking for damage or disconnection.

If there is a spark, you can be reasonably sure that current is reaching the pump. The next check is to take off the plastic top cover and look at the points. They should be closed. If they are not, look for stiffness in the contact-breaker mechanism.

If the points are touching and there are still no signs of life from the pump, it is possible that the points are worn or corroded. A temporary cure can be effected by cleaning the points surfaces with fine emery cloth.

Complete overhaul of the pump is possible as a do-it-yourself exercise but make sure, before you start, that you can get the necessary parts. They are not easy to buy, as some makers believe that the pump should be completely replaced. A good local auto-electrician could probably help. JJ

From Brooklands to Bonneville

Below: Goldie Gardner *(also pictured above)* and his MG at Bonneville

THOUGH ALL HIS MAJOR RECORDS were broken in cars that were basically MGs in origin, Lt-Col A. T. G. Gardner (universally known as Goldie), born in 1899, was one of the most versatile and ingenious speed merchants of the 1930s and 1940s, and was especially adept at modifying an engine so that it could become eligible for widely differing capacity classes.

Long before he came to the public notice with his speed records, Gardner was an enthusiastic competitor at Brooklands with a variety of light cars, beginning with an Austin Seven in 1924. Seven years later, he had acquired a C-type MG, and he became the first man to lap the outer circuit at Brooklands at over 100 mph in a 750 cc car with it.

Out-and-out racing, found Gardner, had an adverse effect on his right leg, which had been badly wounded during World War I, in which he had won the Military Cross. After a bad crash in the 1932 Tourist Trophy, he withdrew from road racing, though continuing to make the occasional appearance at Brooklands, notching up such successes as third place in the 1934 500-miles race, with an MG K3 Magnette. Indeed, he became vice-president of the British Racing Drivers' Club after World War II. Soon after, Gardner acquired a rather special Magnette, formerly raced by R. T. Horton, which had single-seat bodywork, and lapped Brooklands at over 120 mph. A new, more streamlined body was fitted to this car in 1936, and Gardner raised his Brooklands lap speed to 124.4 mph, a record in the 1100 cc class which remained unbeaten until the track closed in 1939.

However, the car could go faster yet, and in record runs at Montlhéry and Frankfurt in 1937 Gardner clocked almost 150 mph. Nevertheless his sights were set higher still. The following year, he had a new record-breaking car, which was substantially George Eyston's 1934 *Magic Magnette* with a new body, specially rebuilt by MG for him to use.

He reached 186.6 mph at Frankfurt, an achievement which won him both the BRDC Gold Star and the RAC Segrave Trophy, capping this in 1939 with what *The Motor* described as 'one of the finest bits of motoring of all time'. This was his flying kilometre speed of 203.54 mph on the Dessau autobahn—with an engine of just under 1100 cc! He immediately had the engine rebored to just over 1100 cc so that he could annex records in the 1500 cc category as well!

What 1100 cc could do, reckoned Gardner, 750 cc could *nearly* do, so he had a 750 cc six-cylinder unit built to prove his case. The intervention of the war, however, meant that this project had to be shelved for the duration.

After a wartime career as a gunner, Goldie Gardner got his 750 cc record car on the road as quickly as possible. In 1946, on the new Jabbeke motorway in Belgium, Gardner reached 159.15 mph; the next year he returned, with the car now converted to a 500 cc four-cylinder by the simple expedient of removing two conrods and pistons and blanking off two pots. Naturally, he set up new records, reaching 118 mph. In September 1948, he was back at Jabbeke, though the engine under the bonnet of his streamlined MG was from Coventry, rather than Abingdon—it was a prototype of the famous Jaguar twin-cam engine, first seen in the XK120 at the London Motor Show a month later. He reached 176.6 mph, and was awarded a second BRDC Gold Star (although it is fair to add that a year later an XK120 Jaguar went a good deal faster still at Jabbeke).

Shortly afterwards, Gardner was awarded the OBE. By this time, he was back to rebuilding MG engines; a 1000 cc six-cylinder power unit became a 500 cc three-cylinder engine under the Gardner treatment, and achieved a record 154 mph plus.

Next to receive the treatment was a 1-litre, four-cylinder engine from a 1949 MG; transformed into a 500 cc twin, this clocked 121 mph at Jabbeke in the streamliner. Gardner now had records in six out of ten international capacity classes, all taken with his famous MG.

With a blown MG-TD 1500 cc power unit, the car attained 137 mph at Bonneville Salt Flats in 1951; at the same venue a year later, Gardner, now aged 63, reached 148.7 mph with a 2-litre Wolseley engine and 189.5 mph with a new TD unit (which would have been at least 30 mph faster, but for wheelspin on the salt).

With that, the indomitable Gardner called it a day, and devoted himself to his motor-trade interests. He died in 1958, after a long illness, in Eastbourne, Sussex.   DBW

Frank Gardner / WHO'S WHO

King of the 'big banger'

Above: Frank Gardner in action at Silverstone in 1973, driving the giant Group 2 Chevrolet Camaro of 7½ litres

FEW DRIVERS CAN BOAST a longer or more honourable racing career than Australia's Frank Gardner, who took up motor racing in 1949 and, in 1974 at 43, was still performing on the tracks.

Gardner was born in Sydney, Australia on 1 October 1931, the son of a trawler skipper, so it was natural that his formative years should have been spent on or in the sea where he became an expert swimmer, oarsman and surfer. He graduated from technical college with a degree in mechanical engineering and gravitated to an uncle who ran a transport business. His uncle's garage housed various racing cars, for he was a keen motor-racing enthusiast; by the age of seventeen, the young Gardner was at the wheel of an MG TA in his first race—which he won with ease. However, he still kept up his water sports as well as boxing, and he even found time to take up speedway racing on motor cycles.

Frank started his own small garage business and in 1953 bought an XK120 and started serious motor racing. This car was replaced by a C-type Jaguar which helped him to win the New South Wales Sports Car Championship, before being sold to Frank Matich and succeeded by a D-type Jaguar. The D-type powered Gardner to numerous wins and two more New South Wales Championships in 1956 and 1957.

The lure of European racing appealed to the still-youthful Gardner, so he sold up and headed for England where, after touring around for a while, he took a job with Aston Martin, working on their sports-racing cars. This was followed by a spell with Jim Russell, and his first few drives in England, at the wheel of a Lotus 18 Formula Junior car. Jack Brabham then asked Gardner to join him in the new Brabham team, so Gardner built the Brabham FJ cars, also managing to race one. Successes were now coming fairly regularly in the FJ Brabhams. He also won the Index of Thermal Efficiency at Le Mans in 1962 driving a Lotus Elite. He spent 1963 with the Ian Walker team, driving FJ Brabhams with Paul Hawkins and picking up a fair number of wins in the process. He also raced the first Brabham sports car, again with some success. For 1964, he signed with the Willment team driving Ford saloons, Lotus and Brabham F2 cars and an AC Cobra GT. He collected a mixed bag of wins and went back home to Australia in the winter to take part in the Tasman series in a 2½-litre Brabham-Climax, picking up several places and second overall in the Tasman Championship.

Frank made it into Formula One in 1965 with a Brabham-BRM run by Willment, but the team lacked the resources to prepare it properly and a fourth place in the Race of Champions was his only decent result of the year. He had more luck at the wheel of a Formula Two Lola which he drove for the Midland Racing Partnership.

By 1966, Gardner had been contracted to Ford to drive for Alan Mann Racing and he had a mixed season at the wheel of Ford GT40s, Lotus Cortinas and a Ford Falcon, but had better luck in the Tasman Series where he finished up joint second in a Brabham-Climax.

He was now regarded as a fine all rounder and was often called up by teams who wanted a good, reliable driver. In 1967, he drove a works F2 Brabham, almost winning the European F2 title, but he did win the British Saloon Car Championship in one of Mann's Ford Falcons. He also drove a GT40, Lola T70 and American stock cars as well as testing F1 Brabhams for the works. His value as a test driver was now being recognised and many teams asked him to try a recalcitrant car to discover its problems.

He raced a Brabham-Alfa Romeo in the 1967/68 Tasman series, achieving several places. In Europe during 1968, he won the British Saloon Car Championship again, this time with an Alan Mann Ford Escort. Gardner also drove F1 Cooper-Maserati and BRM cars on occasions, but they were outclassed and he decided that Formula One cars were not for him, so he never raced them again. For the next few years, he concentrated on saloon-car racing, driving an Escort again in 1969, as well as Mike de Udy's Lola-Chevrolet, which gained him several wins.

For 1970, Ford brought a Boss Mustang to Britain and Gardner, now established in his own engineering business, developed it quickly into a race winner, only just failing to win the British Championship. The Lola factory asked him to sort out the troublesome Lola T190 Formula 5000 single seater and this he did by lengthening the wheelbase and making many other modifications. He then won several races with the car, much to the delight of Lola boss Eric Broadley, who offered him a job at the factory.

In 1971, he developed the new Lola T300 F5000 car and notched up several good wins to take the European F5000 Championship, while he also drove a Chevrolet Camaro to numerous wins in saloon-car events. He took a Lola T300 to the Tasman Series and won the New Zealand Grand Prix, but a bad crash at Levin persuaded him to give up single-seater racing.

Since then, Gardner has concentrated on his Chevrolet Camaro, winning numerous races in Britain, taking the 1972 Tarmac Championship and third place in the British Championship with several overall wins out of a possible ten. He repeated his win in the Tarmac Championship in 1973, again using a Chevrolet Camaro, but the limitation on engine capacity in saloon-car races, and the rise of Group One racing restricted Gardner's appearances in the big Camaro. However, he intended, in 1974, to continue for a little longer, keeping his hand in with routine testing of the new racing cars built by Lola.

When he does decide to retire, Frank Gardner's salty repartee and fund of good stories will be missed almost as much as his skill at the wheel of big racing cars.   MT

WHO'S WHO/Garlits

Drag's Charger

Above: Don Garlits, perhaps the best known drag racer of all time. Garlits has been involved in drag racing for many years

IT IS SLIGHTLY IRONIC that, although he has probably released more horsepower onto tarmac than any other motor sportsman in history, Don Garlits is almost unknown outside America. The sport in which he achieved equal measures of fame and fortune in his home country is drag racing, the supercharged standing-start plunge down a flat quarter-mile strip.

Garlits was born in Tampa, Florida, on 14 January 1932. His father was an engineer who had gone to Florida, like so many others, to try and get rich by fruit farming. 1932 saw his orange-growing business collapse under a combined attack from fruit flies and his bank, so young Don did not quite get a de luxe introduction to life. The family scratched by though, and Don eased through his early years, acquiring a reasonable education and a loose interest in hot rods by the time he was seventeen. The trouble was that he and his friends rarely saw one: it was strictly a West Coast fad.

A few years after Garlits had left school and passed through a few abortive jobs, hot rods really started to catch the kids' interest in Florida. Garlits and his friends all had them, and their main source of fun was rushing around Tampa at all hours of day and night, racing each other at traffic lights and drive-ins.

Soon, they found their own place to race off the street, and the Tampa kids set up a drag strip just like the ones they had read about in magazines from California. Garlits stayed in and around the hot rod/drag-racing scene, driving faster and faster and learning more and more about what made cars flash down that 440 yard strip just those few fractions of a second faster. In 1955, he won his first major title—Top Eliminator, Zephyr Hills Raceway—and suddenly Don Garlits was in drag racing in a big way. Building and racing drag cars became his career, and the next couple of years were spent taking more titles, although he never strayed far out of Florida in those early professional days.

In 1957, he took his car to a National meeting in Illinois and served notice that in future he was going to be the man to beat, by almost taking the Top Eliminator title once again, this time, against very stiff opposition. He still was not making much money out of the sport though, and had to relay on his mechanical skill and innovative powers to keep him up with the front runners. Cars were, by now, running at well over 150 mph and recording sub-nine-second times for the quarter. All kinds of new tricks were being tried to shave off those vital few milliseconds. At about this time, some of the drivers were switching to dragsters with engines in the rear, but Garlits did not think much of the idea then. Several years later he changed his mind completely.

In 1959, Garlits had his first serious accident, at a race in Chester, South Carolina. A bad fire, caused by a ruptured manifold at over 170 mph, put him in hospital for several weeks with serious burns, and changed the whole attitude of the drag-racing world towards protective clothing.

It did not deter him though, and he started running a team of cars. People like Art Malone and Connie Swingle drove his cars with repeated success and his reputation as a builder increased, despite reluctance by the Californian faction to accept him as a top ranker.

In 1960, he retired briefly after spinning his car at 165 mph and dealing his confidence a serious blow. It was a short-lived lay-off though, and he was back in the hot seat before too many months had passed. Soon, he was running as strong as ever, but 1960 and 1961 were not particularly good years for him, dogged as they were with ill-luck and a long string of breakages. Another fire in 1961 put him back in hospital for a short time, and for most of that year he concentrated mainly on building replicas of his car, dubbed 'Swamp Rat', for customers.

1963 saw him back with a vengeance though, and a big bundle of sponsorship money as well. It was a good year in terms of racing successes, especially when he became the first man to break the 200 mph barrier on the dragstrip. 1964 was equally good, with Garlits taking the National title and even managing a trip to England, along with several other top American drag-racing stars. They delighted the English fans, and laid the groundwork for development in the UK.

The following year was a bad one. Many defeats and a bad accident at a strip in Maryland kept him out of the headlines and there was much talk of him being past it. After all, he had already been a front runner for ten years. The critics could not have been more wrong though. The remaining years of the sixties passed, and Garlits was always on or near the top.

The early seventies saw him in another serious accident, this time losing part of one foot when a differential on his car exploded. This time it seemed as if he really was finished, but before too long he was back on the strip once more, with the resolve that he would never drive a front-engined car again.

It was not long before he clawed his way back to the top and, in 1974, he staggered his fans and critics alike by arriving at the Supernationals in California, unloading his car and going straight out to record a time of 5.80 seconds straight away! Sub-six second times had been recorded already, but such a low time was quite unprecedented. Once again, Don Garlits, Big Daddy to his fans, was the talk of the drag-racing world—at forty-two years of age.

AA

Gasket / HOW IT WORKS

PROVIDING AN EFFICIENT FLUID SEAL

There are a great many joints in a motor car, which are required to keep fluids in or out. The easiest way to make these impervious is to use a gasket.

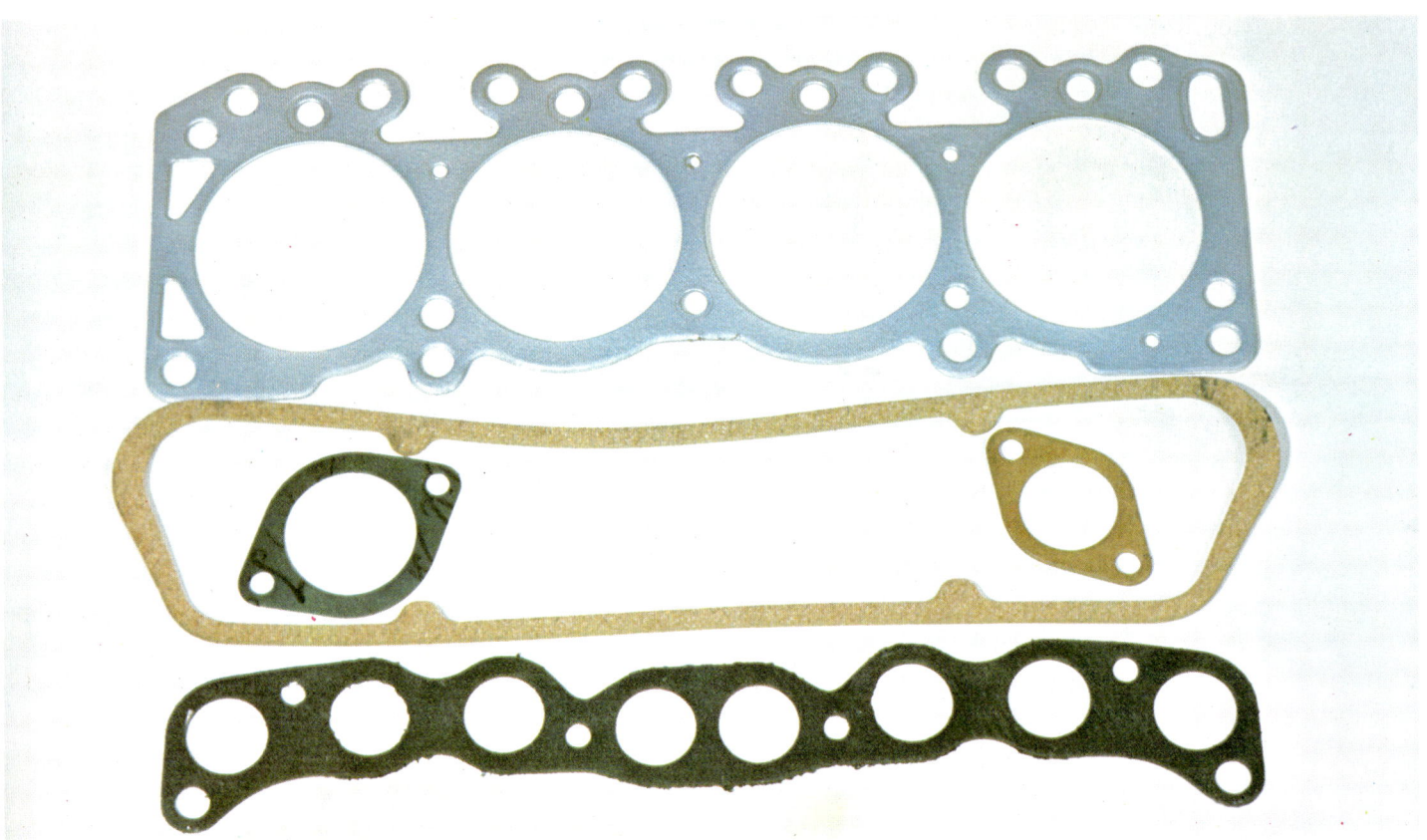

A gasket set for all the parts concerned with a car's cylinder head. At the top is the head gasket itself; below that is the cork gasket for the rocker cover; within that are two gaskets for the carburettor and thermostat housing; at the bottom is the metal and fibre gasket for the inlet and exhaust manifolds

WHERE TWO OR MORE PARTS of an engine meet, or where an auxiliary is bolted on and fluid passes through, there is the possibility of leakage. In most cases, this is prevented by sandwiching a gasket between the two parts. The engine manufacturer does as much as he can to ensure that two parts fit closely, by machining the two surfaces flat, but a gasket is still necessary to prevent slight weepages, especially as the joint can be subject to many pressures. Gaskets are put in an engine to seal between the cylinder head and the rocker cover, between the head and crankcase, the crankcase and sump, under the mating edges of the water pump and timing chain cover and under components like the oil pump, oil-filter housing and thermostat cover. They may also be found in many other components such as the carburettor.

Depending on its location in the engine and the job it has to do, the materials of which the gasket is made vary. Where it is a case of preventing oil from leaking out, the gasket is often made of thin sheet cork; the sealing around the rocker cover and around the flange of the sump cover are examples of this.

When the liquid inside is water, very often the sealing gasket is made from thin paper material. Instances of use include sealing under the thermostat-housing cover and between water pump and crankcase. The thickness of the gasket often varies, too, and sometimes it can be a thick, compressed-paper-type composition.

When exhaust gases have to be coped with, gaskets are usually an asbestos composition or perhaps metal. You will find these positioned between the exhaust manifold and the head or between the exhaust manifold and the exhaust pipe flange.

The most complex and critical gasket of all, and one which has not been described yet, is positioned between the head and the crankcase. The facing surfaces of both components are machined flat and the gasket has to cope with combustion gas, water and oil pressures. The usual type of gasket comprises two very thin sheets of copper, sandwiching a layer of asbestos. Holes are made through the gasket to accommodate the cylinder bores, water passages, oil ways (not in every case), pushrod galleries and head studs or bolts. To keep the asbestos sheet between the copper layers, one sheet of copper is wrapped over onto the other, the same technique being used around all the cut holes.

Fitting a head gasket demands a lot of care. Both the surface of the head and the crankcase must be clean and

HOW IT WORKS/Gasket

free from all traces of the old gasket, gasket cement or carbon. Ensure the gasket goes on the right way up—it often has TOP stamped on it. This is important because if fitted upside down, it could block some vital water passages.

When the head is in position, the correct sequence for tightening the bolts must be observed. Generally, this starts in the centre and works diagonally outwards, but a numbered sequence is given for most cars in the appropriate workshop manual. In addition to tightening the bolts in the correct sequence, it is important that all the bolts should be tightened to the correct pressure or torque. To do this you must use a torque wrench and tighten down to the torque figure recommended by the manufacturer. This will be given in pounds feet.

Head gaskets usually 'bed down' after the engine has been running for a while. At about 300–400 miles, the head bolts should be checked and retightened.

Some engines use a solid copper or solid steel gasket which is thinner than the usual copper/asbestos sandwich and gives a higher compression ratio. In these instances, carefully machined and cleaned surfaces are even more important.

Generally, head gaskets go in position without any additional fixing or sealing, but occasionally a manu-

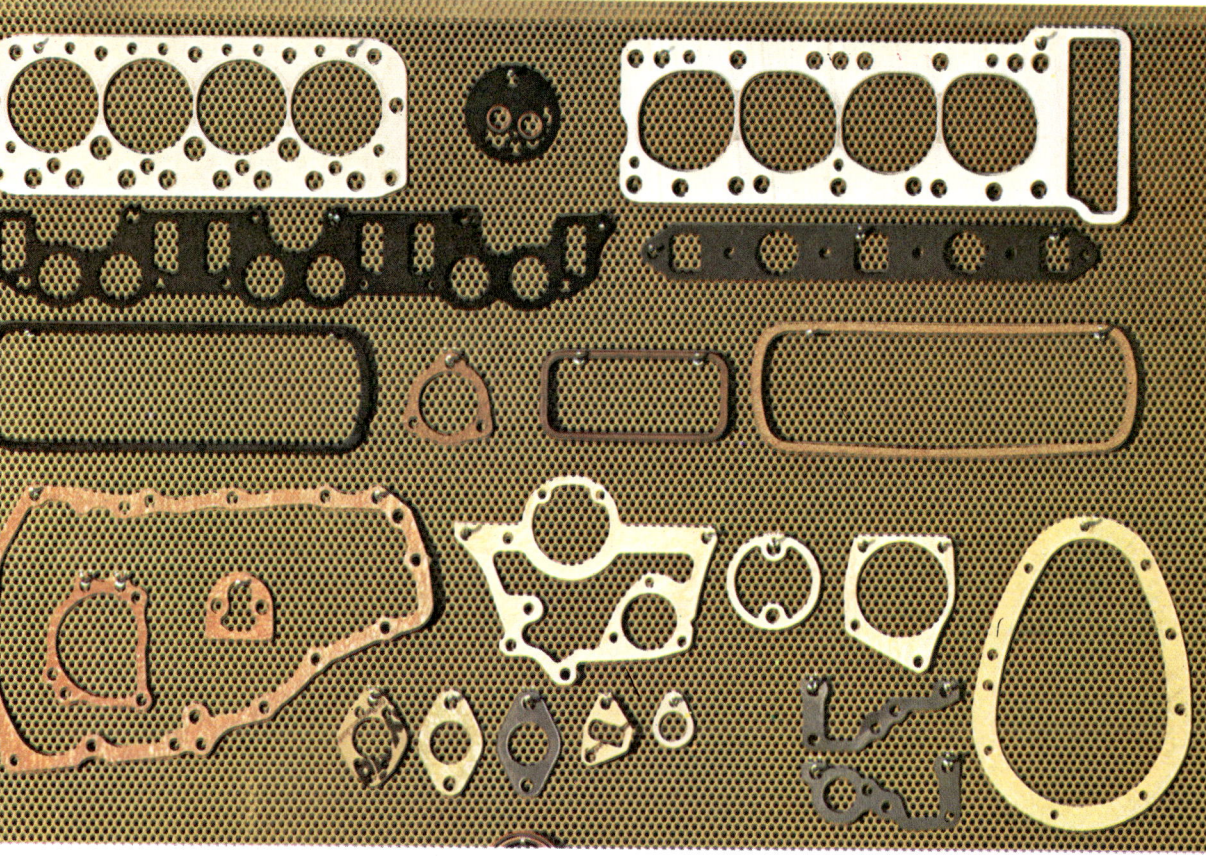

Left: a large selection of gaskets made of materials such as copper, cork, asbestos and paper

Below left: gaskets of today can be bought in neatly packaged sets, comprising just the parts required

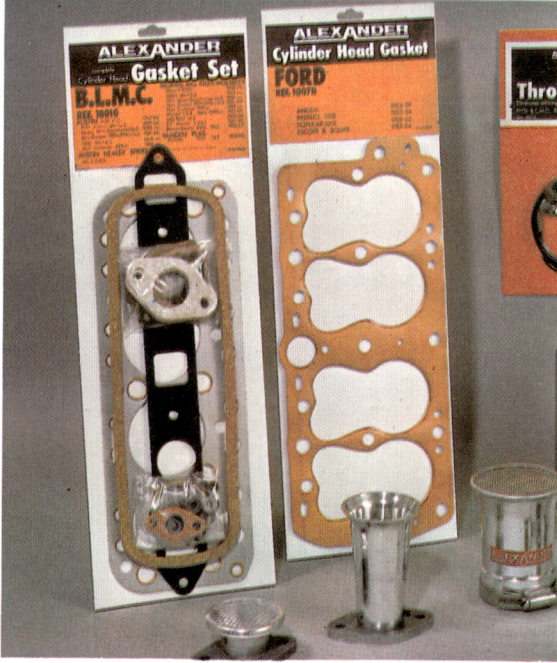

facturer will specify gasket cement. This filler/adhesive is more commonly used with paper gaskets, the usual technique being to spread the compound on one side of the gasket only. Here, again, clean flat surfaces, free from all traces of old gasket and cement, are vital.

Gaskets are sold separately if required, or in sets. If the top end of an engine is being rebuilt, you will need a 'decoke set' and if the engine is being rebuilt completely, a 'sump set' will be needed in addition.

While gaskets for most cars are readily obtainable from most shops, difficulty can sometimes be experienced. This is when it is important to realise that homemade gaskets can be used. Copper/asbestos head gaskets and the like will require the service of a specialist manufacturer, but you can make your own cork gaskets or paper types.

The usual way to do this is to use the machined flange of one of the mating faces as a pattern. If the sheet of gasket material is hammered lightly onto the pattern, an imprint will be left on it, or perhaps, the sharp edges of the casting may cut the gasket out. If cutting is not complete the job can be finished using a craft knife on a smooth hard surface. A smear of paint on the pattern surface will help define the shape.   JJ

Gas turbine/HOW IT WORKS

THE ULTIMATE ROTARY ENGINE?

The gas turbine is probably the smoothest-running of the internal-combustion engines and it runs on cheap fuel; but there are great drawbacks

TAKE A PISTON ENGINE and add, in the quest for greater power and thermal efficiency and cleaner exhausts, an exhaust-driven turbocharger. In exchange for a greater exhaust back pressure, the boosted engine will deliver more power. If it be a good and suitable engine, and well matched by the turbocharger, it may be possible to go on and on increasing both back pressure and power until the stage be reached where the exhaust turbine driving the supercharger impeller is delivering as much power as the engine crankshaft. When this stage is reached, it becomes logical to pursue further increases by treating the turbine shaft as the power output and leaving the engine shaft to drive the supercharger. The engine and supercharger together then constitute merely a gas-producing unit feeding the exhaust turbine. Why not then substitute a rotary compressor and a continuous combustion chamber for the cylinders and pistons of the engine, eliminating all the problems of reciprocating parts, vibration, intermittent respiration and combustion, and so on?

This was the reasoning that led to the evolution, rather than the invention, of the gas turbine. The answer to the question 'Why not?' was simply metallurgical: it was a long time before materials could be developed that would stand the combination of mechanical and thermal stresses imposed by such a power plant. It was World War II and its aftermath which gave materials technology the necessary impetus, and now the gas turbine is an accepted means of propelling aircraft and ships at high speeds, and of providing emergency power for electricity generators and fire pumps. Where high operating efficiency (especially thermal efficiency), light weight, exceptional reliability and fairly constant conditions of operating speed and load are concerned, the cost of making a gas turbine from the expensive materials required and with the accuracy of blade formation necessary—not to mention the cost of installation, with elaborate control apparatus which may account for one third of the total cost in an aircraft—is justifiable. Even on grounds of lightness alone, the gas turbine is worth having in a commercial aircraft, where the saving of one pound in weight is worth the expenditure of £20 capital. In a commercial vehicle such as a lorry, limited by law to a certain weight, but deriving its income from the largest payload it can carry, each pound weight saved may be worth £4. Private cars offer no such temptation: with scarcely any exceptions they are all made as cheaply as possible, the minimisation of capital cost far outweighing all other considerations, and there would be very few customers for an inevitably costly gas-turbine engine.

The conditions in which a car engine works are not in any case suitable for the gas turbine. Operating speed and load vary almost continually, making it unlikely that the high thermal efficiency attainable when running at or near full power could be realised. A gas turbine develops a terrible thirst when running

light, as it would usually have to do in a car; it also responds very slowly to changes in load. Finally, there is no premium on reliability in private cars: whatever the customers may say, they know that a mechanical failure usually involves no more than inconvenience (as opposed to the probability in aviation of falling out of the sky) and they are not disposed to pay a lot for the probability of evading what is merely a possibility. The reliability of the gas turbine is not worth the cost to the customer.

Of course there have been turbine-powered cars. Rover, Renault, Fiat and Chrysler all experimented briefly with the idea; but, although the car ran well enough, they seemed sops to public gullibility rather than serious engineering programmes. Rover did most: employing the chassis expertise and competition experience of BRM, they produced a small turbine-engined two-seater for the 24-hour Le Mans race. The little car went spectacularly well, and was promptly dismissed by the traditionalists and know-alls as a thing of no moment and even less future. Even the

Above left: the Rover company has always been in the vanguard of motor manufacturers experimenting with the gas-turbine engine as an alternative power source to the reciprocating engine. This is the Rover T4 turbine model, the engine of which is situated in the front of the car

HOW IT WORKS/Gas turbine

Above: turbine-engined Rovers about to start a demonstration run during a race meeting at the Silverstone Grand Prix circuit. In the foreground is JET 1 the first of Rover's turbine models. Just poking its nose into the left hand side of the picture is the 1963 Le Mans Rover–BRM turbine car

drivers, who found that the only way to keep the engine responsive enough for instant acceleration out of corners was to hold the accelerator pedal down all the way round the circuit and simply slow the car by heaving on the brakes with the other foot, must have readily agreed.

Nothing more was seen or heard of the gas turbine until one day in 1967 when the Indianapolis 500 miles race featured a car so powered. This was the STP-sponsored chassis with a Paxton turbine and Parnelli Jones in it—and he was incredulous enough, reporting that for the first time in his long racing experience he could hear the suspension working. The car went almost unheard, its soft whistle drowned by the tumultuous moan of the spectators, the groans of frustration from the other team managers, and the frantic sound of hyper-tuned piston engines straining to keep in sight of the turbine-engined car. It was an epoch-marker—until just before the end, when a minor and insignificant bearing failure put the car out of the race when comfortably in the lead. The establishment recovered quickly and, whilst declaring that the gas turbine was obviously not competitive, quickly re-wrote the rules to ensure that it remained so. When Lotus came to Indianapolis with a team of less powerful Pratt & Whitney turbine-engined racers, they nevertheless dominated the event almost to the end, but then, after a period of slow cruising under the notorious Indianapolis 'yellow flag' safety rules, the sudden imposition of full load when the track was clear caused both surviving Lotuses (the third had crashed) to suffer a flame-out. The race was lost, the cause was lost, and we heard nothing more until an adapted version of one of these cars ran in several Grands Prix, proving utterly uncompetitive in the manifestly unsteady conditions of European road racing. Following this, no attempt has been made to continue their development in racing.

Since then the gas turbine has only been considered for trucks, which for some duties can exploit the high power, the light weight and the low fuel consumption of a gas turbine running consistently at or near full

749

Gas turbine / HOW IT WORKS

Above left: designed by Ray Heppenstall of Philadelphia, the Howmet turbine car was raced at Le Mans in 1968, but failed to finish

Above right: Jackie Stewart and Graham Hill drove this turbine-engined Rover–BRM to tenth place in the 1965 Le Mans 24-hour endurance event

Above: operated by the Burmah Castrol Company, and built by Leyland Motors Ltd, this outfit is fitted with a Leyland Turbine 6×4 prime mover, complete with a 350–400 bhp gas-turbine engine

load. Motorway trunking, heavy haulage across Russia or Australia or the USA, offer opportunities for the turbine truck; and both Ford and British Leyland have been active in the pursuit of ideas for high-powered freight tractors.

A feature of both is the simplicity of the compressor stages. In an aviation turbine, the compressor commonly has row after row of blades, each row increasing the mass air flow into the combustion chamber. In these truck turbines there is merely one centrifugal compressor and two axial-flow turbines with a row of static blades between. The compressor feeds air to the combustion chamber where fuel is continuously injected and continuously burnt; the gas produced by combustion then expands through the first turbine, which is fixed to the shaft driving the compressor. This turbine is designed to take no more than the power needed to sustain the compressor; the rest of the potential in the combustion gases is exploited by the second turbine, which is attached to the output shaft. The static blades between the turbine rotors are arranged to control the flow of gas, and they can be varied in pitch so far that the power turbine is blown the wrong way, producing a form of engine-powered braking that may compensate for the absence of conventional engine braking.

This attractive simplicity has to be measured against a probable loss of efficiency, because only the best and most complex of aviation turbines attain the high expansion ratio which ensures satisfactory fuel economy. The expansion ratio is analogous to what we call the compression ratio in ordinary car engines. In an automotive diesel the figure is often 18:1 or more, whereas the simplified compressor of these automotive turbines allows a ratio of no more than 4:1. This could be translated into a grave handicap in the form of impossibly heavy fuel consumption (even though the fuel could be cheap and have a low fire risk), especially poor in conditions of low power demand. Yet the Leyland consumes only 0.392 lb of fuel per horsepower per hour when running at 85% maximum power, and the Ford is comparable—as they both are with diesels, which can often manage only 0.4 lb/hp h.

The secret is in two slowly-rotating discs of glass ceramics. These are the regenerative heat exchangers, which recover much of the waste heat from the exhaust efflux and feed it back into the air that is being led to the combustion chamber. These heat exchangers tend to be as bulky as the turbine itself, and it is arguable that they are a step towards the loss of that basic simplicity which is a prime attraction of the turbine. Certainly they are vulnerable to thermal and

HOW IT WORKS/Gas turbine

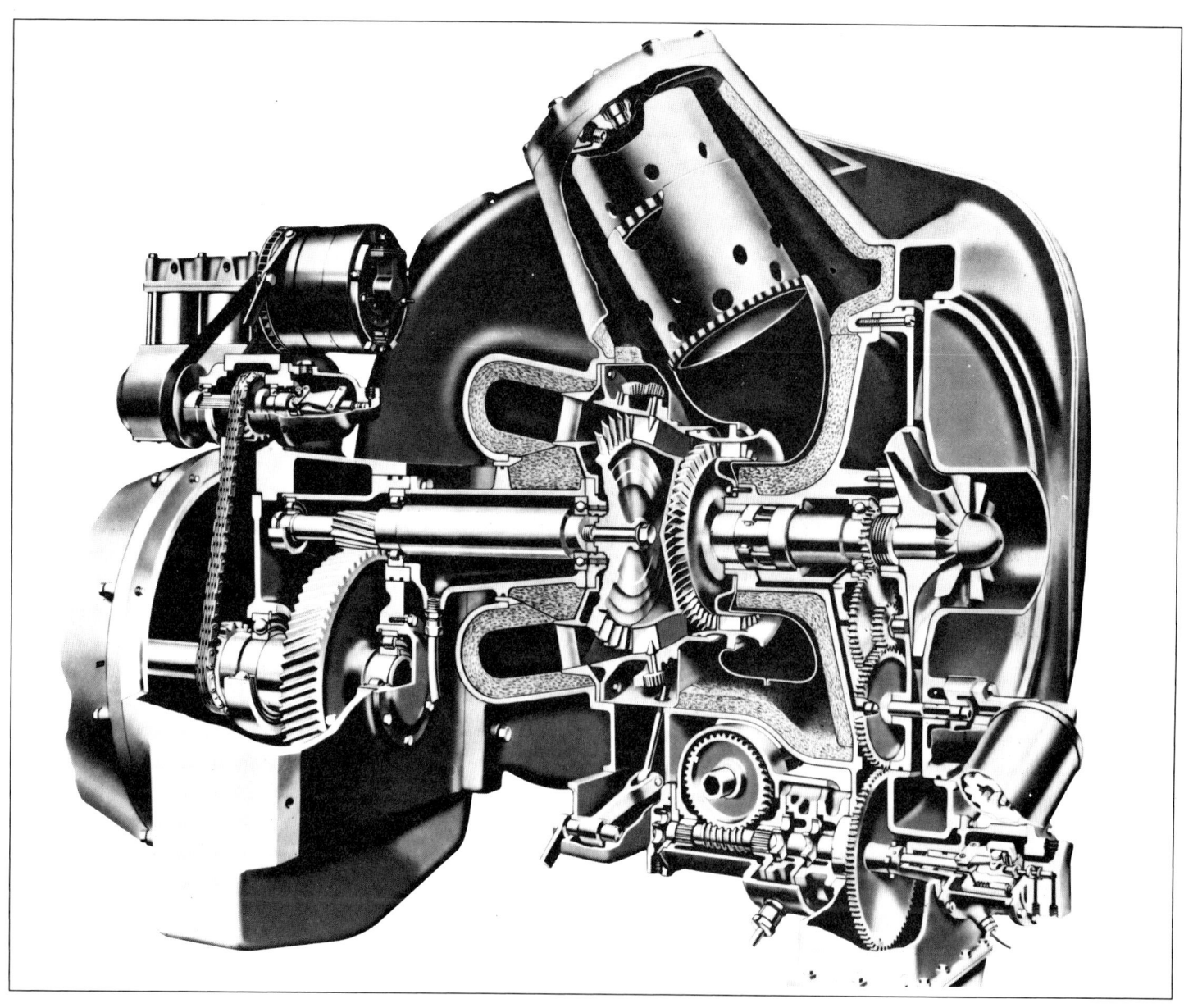

Above: the British Leyland 25/350/R gas-turbine engine develops between 350 and 400 bhp and weighs under 454 kg, approximately half that of a comparable diesel unit. The life expectancy of the engine before a major overhaul is about 12,000 running hours, equal to well over 500,000 miles

mechanical shock, but they are indispensable: the heat they transmit to the intake air raises its pressure (as the only possible alternative to expanding it, which is impossible) and thus does as much as any number of extra compressor stages. Without these heat exchangers, the Ford and Leyland turbines would have to be built to achieve a pressure ratio of 16:1 to perform as well as they do at 4:1.

In these 'two-spool' turbines (which are most suitable to automotive duties, where the compressor and the turbine driving it are mounted on a shaft that is separate from the power turbine which is furthest downstream), the power turbine works as an efficient torque converter, making elaborate transmission gearboxes unnecessary. As the rotational speed of the power turbine is reduced by road load, the torque output is increased: with the compressor shaft running at full speed and power, the power shaft may offer when stationary a torque as much as 2½ times greater than it gives when running at full speed. In other words the gas turbine is a constant-power unit, with torque back-up characteristics like those of a steam engine. This is virtually ideal for vehicle propulsion—but only so long as the engine is running at or near full power, and only so long as the ambient air temperature is low, and even then only if the control apparatus for the variable pitch stator blades is complex enough to ensure satisfactory performance. Otherwise, the fall-off in performance can be crippling, and the only other good thing to be said about the turbine is that its exhaust is fairly clean and its smoothness impeccable.

Other problems have by now been mastered. Heat soak to the bearings after engine shut-down used to be one, cured by an auxiliary pump that keeps the bearings flooded with fresh cool oil for some time after the engine has stopped. The costly and intransigent metals needed to withstand the high temperatures and enormous centrifugal stresses can be replaced to a large extent by ceramics arranged to be loaded in compression (when they are mechanically stable) rather than in tension (when they shatter at the slightest provocation, as from an ingested foreign body). Although enthusiastic visionaries foretell the day of the small gas turbine only three inches in diameter, packed with ceramics rotors spinning in inert-gas bearings and propelling our cars at high speeds into a romantic sunset, the cynicism of the realists (who see increasing performance limitations and fuel costs as well as a general disinclination to dally any longer with fancy power plants for customers who are unwilling to spend more) is more likely to eventually prove correct.

LJKS

GAZ/THE GREAT CARS

PART OF THE RUSSIAN REVOLUTION

The irony of the Russian State-owned GAZ company's prosperity is that the credit for this success must go to arch-capitalist Henry Ford

IF, TEN YEARS AFTER THE RUSSIAN REVOLUTION, you had asked a peasant in Tomsk or Smolensk to name the men he most admired, the chances are that the reply would have been Lenin, Trotsky, Kalinin and Henry Ford.

The reason why the arch-capitalist Ford was enshrined among the communist heroes was that the Fordson tractor had contributed hugely to the economic revival of Russia after the Revolution. Over 25,000 of these machines were in use from Leningrad to Vladivostock by 1926, overcoming crop failure and famine, and bringing Russian agricultural methods out of the Middle Ages into the 20th century overnight.

During the 1920s, the Russians began building rather crude ersatz Fordsons under the name Krasny Putilowitz and they invited Ford to set up an assembly plant. He decided against this because of the ever-present threat of nationalisation. However, as a contribution towards world peace and prosperity, Ford was prepared to help the Russians build a new factory in which cars would be built to Ford designs by Ford methods. He would provide detailed plant layouts and working projects for a plant capable of producing 100,000 cars and trucks a year; in return, the Russians agreed to buy 72,000 Ford vehicles over four years through their Amtorg Trading Corporation.

This agreement meant that the Russians would gain an instant motor industry, while Ford, hopefully, would make a modest profit, the cars, trucks and parts supplied being priced at cost plus 15 per cent.

The project became a cornerstone of Stalin's first five-year plan; contracts were signed late in 1929, and assembly of Ford Model A cars and trucks began in a small factory, the KIM works, in Moscow. But this was just the start, for a huge new car works was planned at Nizhni Novgorod, where another assembly plant was located.

Eight miles outside Nizhni (which was renamed Gorkiy in 1932) was a virtually deserted stretch of land between the rivers Volga and Oka; it was here, in 1930, that the Austin Company of Cleveland, Ohio, began work on the new Molotov car works and its attendant workers' city, which could house 25,000 people. Within months, 10,000 labourers were at work on the construction of factory and city, and, despite setbacks caused by material and labour shortages, the plant was ready virtually on time.

These 'Russki-Ford' cars were known as GAZ-A after the new factory (Gorkiy Automobile Zavod); there was also a GAZ-AA truck, followed within a couple of years by the GAZ-AAA six-wheeler. Though the Ford agreement was terminated on 22 November 1934, in accordance with Russian policy on discontinuing direct foreign aid, the Gorkiy factory continued to build Model-A derived trucks until well after the war. Indeed, production emphasis was heavily weighted in favour of trucks, a bias shown by the fact that three-quarters of all vehicles now built in the Soviet Union are commercials.

Nevertheless, there was progress on the passenger car front, under the direction of engineer Andrei Lipgart, whose first design, the GAZ M-1, replaced the GAZ-A in 1936. The M-1 used 1933 Ford body dies to press out its panels, and still had the Model A Ford engine, but the transmission and grille were Russian-designed. A six-cylinder version, the GAZ M-11, appeared in 1938, powered by a six-cylinder 3.5-litre engine; during World War II, versions of this car, which still retained traces of its Ford ancestry, were used as command vehicles. There was also a four-wheel-drive version, built from 1942 until 1948, the GAZ-61 and the GAZ M-1 was modified as a half-track called the Pikap, and nicknamed Vezdekhod ('Go-anywhere'). Standard GAZ cars and trucks also saw military service by the hundred, while the old

Above: the GAZ-A was the first model to be produced by the Russian GAZ factory. The project was the result of an agreement, in 1929, between the Ford Motor Company of America and the Stalin government to produce Ford Model As under licence in Russia

Left: admirably suited to Russian needs, although considered perhaps a little crude by Western standards, this is the 1970 Volga 24. The car uses a four-cylinder 2.5-litre engine

THE GREAT CARS/GAZ

GAZ-AAA chassis was transformed into a four-man armoured car with a 45 mm gun and two machine guns (there was also an amphibious version, the BAZ).

There was also a new vehicle, the GAZ-67, based on the American Jeep, which used the Model A engine in a four-wheel-drive chassis. Its basic design was rather crude, but the vehicle survived in production from 1943 to 1953. It was widely used in the Korean War, and was eventually supplanted by the GAZ-69A.

Meanwhile, back at the GAZ works, the passenger-car side of the business had at last thrown off the old 'Russki-Ford' image with the new Lipgart-designed Pobieda ('Victory') of 1946. This unit-constructed saloon was designed to meet the tremendous post-war demand for cars in Russia; it had a four-cylinder, 2.1-litre engine, three-speed transmission, independent front suspension and a 65 mph top speed. A four-wheel-driven variant, the M-72, appeared in 1955, three years before the Pobieda ceased production at Gorkiy (it continued to be built under licence at Warsaw, however).

Already the Pobieda's replacement was on the production lines; this was the M-21 Volga, again designed by Lipgart, which made extensive use of light alloy in its four-cylinder, 2.5-litre power unit, and carried its crankshaft in five main bearings.

During the 1950s, the Gorkiy Works also produced the ZIM (Zavod Imieni Molotova) luxury model, for those whose place in the party structure did not quite rate them for a ZIS (Russia's pseudo-Packard). The ZIM looked like a just-post-war General Motors product, right down to its radiator grille.

The ZIM was replaced in 1958 by the Chaika ('Seagull'), which followed the ZIS (now renamed the ZIL) in copying Packard styling. Unfortunately, the Packard that GAZ chose to copy turned out to be the 1955 Patrician, an aesthetic disaster of the most vulgar kind; Lipgart, apparently disgusted with the styling of the Chaika, resigned, joining the Moscow engine and vehicle research establishment, NAMI.

A newer, lower Mk II Volga appeared in 1968; again, it looked a little crude to Western eyes, but was admirably suited to the somewhat specialised conditions of the Russian car market.

In the 1970s, the GAZ factory was being expanded to meet the growing demand for private transport in Russia and her satellite states. DBW

Below: the original military GAZ 67 was based on the American jeep and used the Ford Model A engine. It survived in production from 1943 to 1953 and was eventually replaced by the GAZ 69A

Below: derived from the military GAZ 69A is the GAZ 69AM, produced for commercial use behind the Iron Curtain. The side-valve, four-cylinder, 2430 cc engine develops 72 bhp and drives all four wheels

Gear/HOW IT WORKS

A POSITIVE LINK BETWEEN TWO SHAFTS

In every motor car, gears are used to transmit motion from one component to another; these parts offer a positive link without any possibility of slip

DRIVE MAY BE TRANSMITTED from one shaft to another parallel one by drums rotating with each shaft and pressed together at their peripheries. It would not be very positive, relying wholly on friction between the mating surfaces; but if projections on the surface of one were to engage depressions in the other, positivity would be assured. Call these projections teeth, ensuring that they and their corresponding depressions are formed in those mathematically derived shapes which guarantee consistent and continuous meshing and uniformity of pressure at the points of contact, and you have a pair of gears. The larger the diameter (and hence the greater the number of teeth) of the driven one in relation to the driver, the slower will be the rotation and the greater the torque of the driven shaft in relation to the driver; and the whole object of gear sets is to transmit torque with mechanical positivity and with precise control over the increase or decrease of rotational speed and torque in the translation.

This facility is demanded in many parts of a car, and gear sets may accordingly be found not only in the gearbox (which is part of the drive line from engine to wheels) but also in the final drive and differential, inside the engine, in the starter, the windscreen-wiper motor, the steering, the window winders, the speedometer drive, and sometimes in carburettors, petrol pumps, seat belt inertia reels and reclining seat adjusters. Inside the engine, gears are responsible for driving the ignition distributor, the oil pump, sometimes the camshaft(s), and very occasionally in old cars the water pump and dynamo. They provide a very positive drive, but they are more costly to make than such other driving media as chains or belts, and there is an increasing tendency to employ these cheaper means wherever possible.

Nevertheless, gears remain in use wherever loads are high or where the drive has to be transmitted through an angle. Mating gears on parallel shafts is the simplest case (they are then known as spur gears) and allows the readiest substitution of chains or belts, but where the shafts are not parallel—and particularly in the case of the hypoid final-drive (axle) gearing, where the shafts are neither parallel nor in the same plane—gears of more complex formation are generally essential. Gears having their axes at right angles and their teeth cut radially are bevel gears; if their teeth are straight but not radial, they are skew gears, and if the teeth are curved they become spiral bevels. Two bevel gears of equal size (as sometimes found in overhead-camshaft drives) are mitre gears. Spiral gears resemble spur gears but with their teeth cut in an extreme helical form that allows them to mesh in pairs on shafts at right angles, as for example in the oil-pump or distributor drive from a camshaft.

The formation of gear teeth is of critical importance in determining efficiency, noise generation, and lubrication requirements which are usually a function of contact pressure. The tooth form of practically all currently-used gears (in cars, if not elsewhere, for refined forms such as the Russian Novikov have important industrial uses) is called an involute. The shape can be generated by the end of a string unwound tautly from a cylindrical drum. When involute teeth are straight (that is, parallel to the axis of the gearwheel) and correctly meshed, they will contact each other at a level roughly one third of the distance up from root to tip on the pitch circle (which is the effective diameter of the gear); and this contact extends over the full width of the tooth, amounting to a line. Theoretically, this line is of infinitely small area and the pressures between the mating teeth should be infinitely high; but in practice no gear tooth is ever so perfectly formed, and in any case there will be some microscopic distortion giving the contact line a finite width, apart from which there is (or should be!) a

Above left: three crown-wheel-and-pinion sets, used to alter the direction of rotation through ninety degrees (as in the rear axle). On the left is the simplest form, with straight teeth on the bevel gears, while the central pair are spiral cut, a feature which reduces noise and spreads load. The third set also comprises spiral bevel gears, but in this case the pinion is offset relative to the crown wheel to provide improved ground clearance

Above: Double helical, or herringbone gears were favoured by André Citroën, but were very expensive to manufacture. This type of gear combines the advantages of helical-cut and straight-cut gears, without the disadvantages. The pattern is remembered on every Citroën in the form of the famous double-chevron badge affixed to the front

HOW IT WORKS/Gear

Below: the differential unit from an Alfa Romeo 2500 of 1939. Note the spiral-cut crown wheel and the straight-cut spur gears

Below right: two types of gear-cutting equipment: the left-hand is simple while the right-hand is in the form of a screw

film of oil cushioning the contact between two parts.

Such a gear set can be very efficient, transmitting a good 98% of the power fed into it; against all expectations, in view of the limited contact area and somewhat intermittent engagement of teeth in succession, it can also be very strong. These two reasons explain the use of such straight-cut gears in racing engines and transmissions; but the noisiness of straight gears rules them out for most passenger cars, though they can be found in the final drive of the Lamborghini Urraco, for example. A quieter and smoother mesh is afforded by helical teeth, still of involute section but no longer parallel to the shaft axis: they may be thought of as

chevron which is the current Citroën badge.

Although helical teeth figure in most configurations, making the mechanical generation of their forms a matter for advanced mathematical work, and the satisfactory lubrication of them a matter for high-pressure additive treatment of the oil, their manufacture is now highly developed and relies on elaborate metallurgy, expensive tooling and precise heat treatment. Mechanical losses are generally low, which tempts designers to get themselves out of difficulties by sometimes using several trains of gears in succession. About the most consumptive of gear types is the worm, which is an extreme case of helically toothed pinion

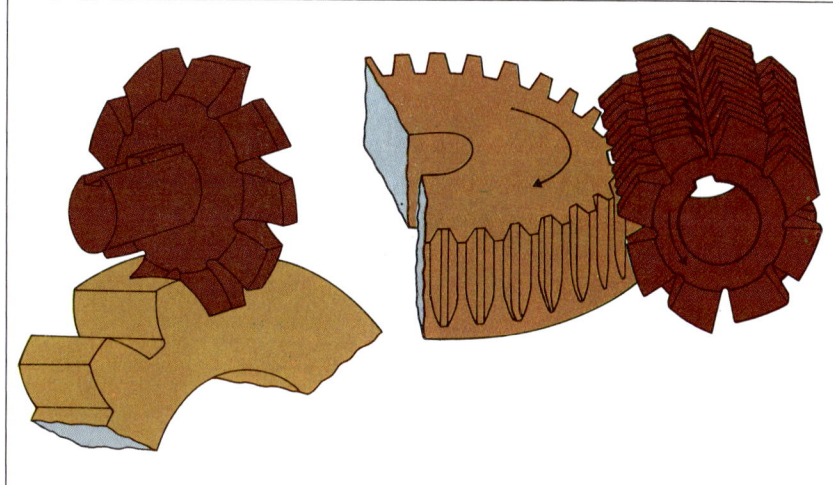

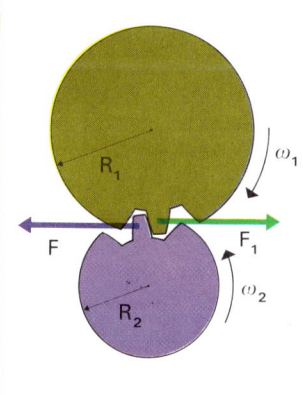

GEAR RELATIONSHIP

The driving wheel (green) transmits the power, $P = M_1 \omega_1$ (M_1 = driving couple: ω_1 = angular velocity of the driving wheel), to the driven wheel, on which it exerts a force, F, equal and opposite to the reaction, F_1. The driven wheel, with a smaller radius, revolves at a velocity ω_1, greater than ω_1, and the couple applied to it is M_2, smaller than M_1 ($P = M_1 \omega_1 = M_2 \omega_2$). For a fixed power figure, as speed increases, torque decreases. The velocity of rotation, ω, is inversely proportional to the radius, R, (or to the number of teeth, z). The torque, M, is directly proportional to the radius, R, (or to the number of teeth, z). The relationship between the gears τ can be illustrated thus:

$$\tau = \frac{\omega_1}{\omega_2} = \frac{R_1}{R_2} = \frac{z_2}{z_1} = \frac{M_2}{M_1}$$

Above: this diagram shows the usual shape of dog teeth used on the faces of non-synchromesh gears. Unless the speeds of the two are equal when engagement takes place, a grating noise will ensue

screw threads of very 'fast' or long pitch. Helical teeth slide over each other, and one pair makes contact before the preceding pair parts: this sliding action promotes friction which reduces the mechanical efficiency and increases the demands made on the lubricating oil. It also creates a side thrust which tends to force the gear wheels axially along their shafts, and if they are fixed to their shafts then the shaft bearings themselves will be subjected to endwise loads and must be designed accordingly. Double helical gears, otherwise known as herringbone gears, create no residual axial thrust but are difficult to make, though they were dear to André Citroën (who employed herringbone bevel gears in the rear axles of some early models) and their pattern survives in the double

(virtually a screw) mating with the peripheral teeth of a large gear on a shaft at right angles to the worm. This arrangement is used only when very large reduction ratios are necessary, although in earlier times it was popular for rear axles.

With automatic transmissions so common, it should be noted that gear teeth may be cut on the inside of a metal ring, as well as on the outside. Internal gears, as they are called, play an important part in some epicyclic gear trains such as feature in automatic gearboxes. A planetary train may consist only of a spur gear (the sun wheel) with another (the planetary wheel) orbiting round it while the arm carrying the planet transmits the output torque; but an internal gear surrounding this planetary set, concentric with the sun wheel and meshing with the planet(s) completes a full epicyclic train. This outermost gear is called the annulus and may be fixed or free to rotate; by clamping or releasing it, or the planet carrier, or the sun wheel, a variety of ratios may be obtained from one gear train.

As a last example of a gear set taken to extremes, consider the occasional need to convert rotation to linear motion. One spur gear, usually the smaller, is left quite normal; the other has its diameter increased to infinity—in other words, it becomes straight, and is then called a rack. Rack and pinion gears are commonplace for steering cars, but their high mechanical efficiency carries with it an extreme reversibility, evident as kick-back at the steering wheel. This may be overcome by frictional damping (hydraulic in expensive cars, occasionally) or by treating the gears as skewed pairs, increasing their inefficiency deliberately. Thus we come to the final point, that the lower the mechanical efficiency of a gear set, the more irreversible it is. Once again, the worm and wheel is the most extreme case, being almost completely irreversible in most examples.

LJKS

Gearbox/HOW IT WORKS

MULTIPLYING THE ENGINE'S FLEXIBILITY

An internal-combustion engine has a speed at which it produces its maximum torque output, so a gearbox is necessary to maintain this engine speed for a range of road speeds

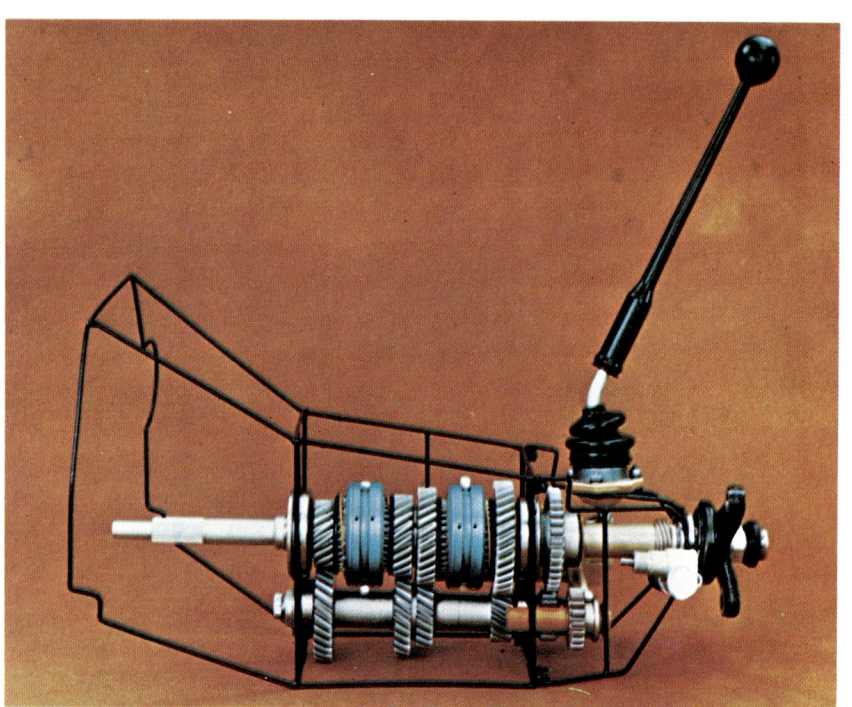

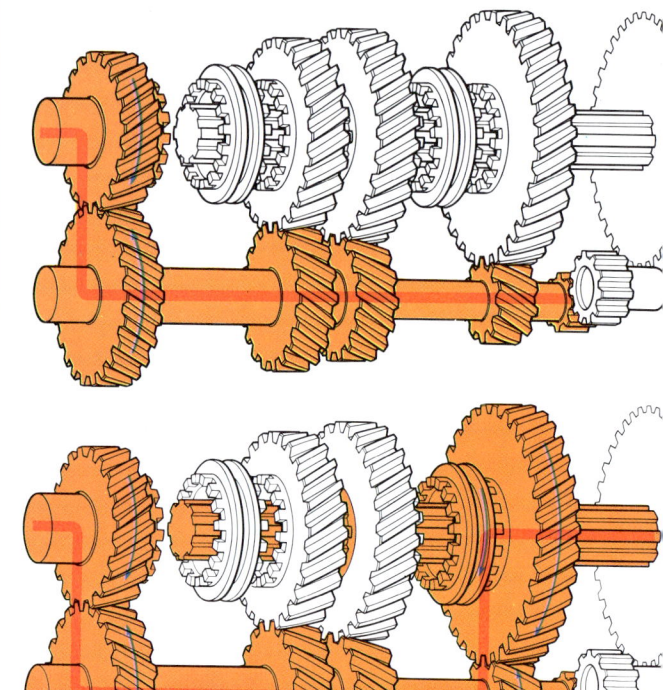

IT IS BRUTAL, BUT IT WORKS was René Panhard's properly scathing comment about the gearbox of his new car, eighty-odd years ago. Some of today's gearboxes are not as advanced as we might reasonably expect, but the majority are designed to suffer brutality rather than to display it. It has been estimated that if as many as sixty per cent of current drivers know why to change gear, only twenty per cent know how and barely five per cent know when. In Panhard's pioneering days, most cars had extremely inflexible engines and changing gear was the only way to vary the speed of the car; that is how the expression 'change speed' became current, so that we still speak of, say, a 'four-*speed* gearbox' when a 'four-*ratio* gearbox' would be more accurate.

What altered the gearchanging habits of the motorist in the vintage era was the evolution of engines whose principle merit was that they breathed well at high revolutions. This was the work of Henry and his associates in the Peugeot design office: his widely emulated overhead-camshaft engines, with four valves per cylinder and fairly mellifluous porting to the pent-roof heads, were alarmingly gutless at low speeds by the standards of the time. In cars designed according to his tenets, the performance at which the peak-power figures hinted could only be realised by keeping the revolutions well up, and this dictated a gearbox with very close ratios. An entirely new style of driving had to be cultivated. In 1908, the internal ratios of a Grand Prix Fiat's four-speed box were typical of those in the gearbox of any large gentlemanly

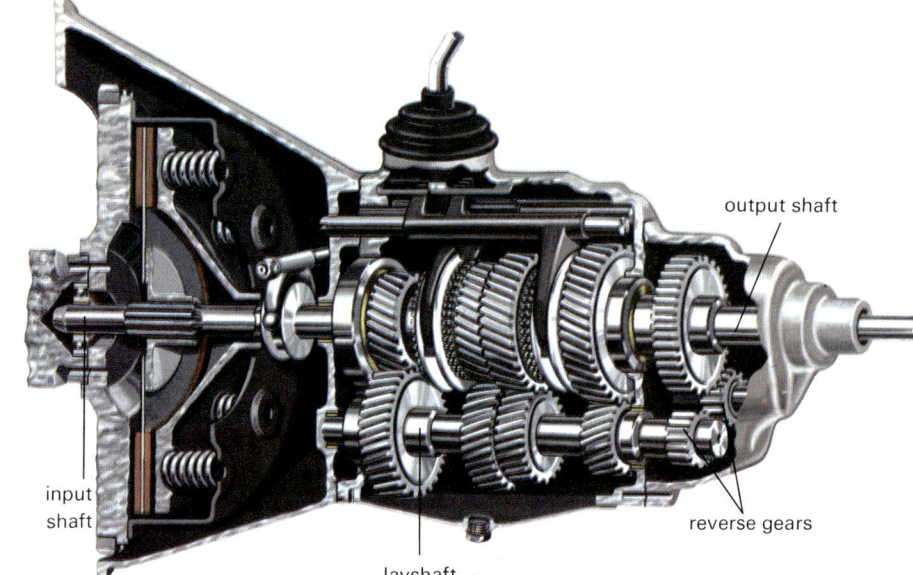

HOW IT WORKS/Gearbox

Far left: the bare bones of a four-speed all-synchromesh gearbox. First and reverse gears are straight cut, while all others are helical

tourer, almost perfectly evenly spaced in increments of about 1.53:1 so that the ratios were 1:1, 1.53:1, 2.38:1 and 3.68:1—but in 1912, the ratios of the GP Peugeot were 1:1, 1.13:1, 1.52:1 and 2.04:1. The Peugeot might not be very electrifying in its acceleration from standstill, but once it was well under way in its 50 mph bottom gear it could be kept pressed up to the bit.

This was the new way to secure really high performance, and the makers of sporting cars duly followed Henry's lead. The early 3-litre Bentley, before it was detuned and castrated for the carriage trade, could be had with gearbox ratios of 1:1, 1.3:1, 1.6:1 and 2.6:1, and the salesmen used to astonish

were communicated by rods or cranks to selector forks which engaged collars on the flanks of the gears: first the dog coupling input to output shafts was moved out of mesh, and then the appropriate spur gear on the output shaft was slid along until its teeth engaged those of the corresponding layshaft gear. Speeding up the engine with the clutch momentarily engaged while the gearlever was in the neutral position would accelerate the rotation of the layshaft (because of the permanently meshed pair of gears) until the speeds of fixed and sliding gears were the same, whereupon they would slide into engagement easily enough. The drive path would then be from input shaft to layshaft and thence

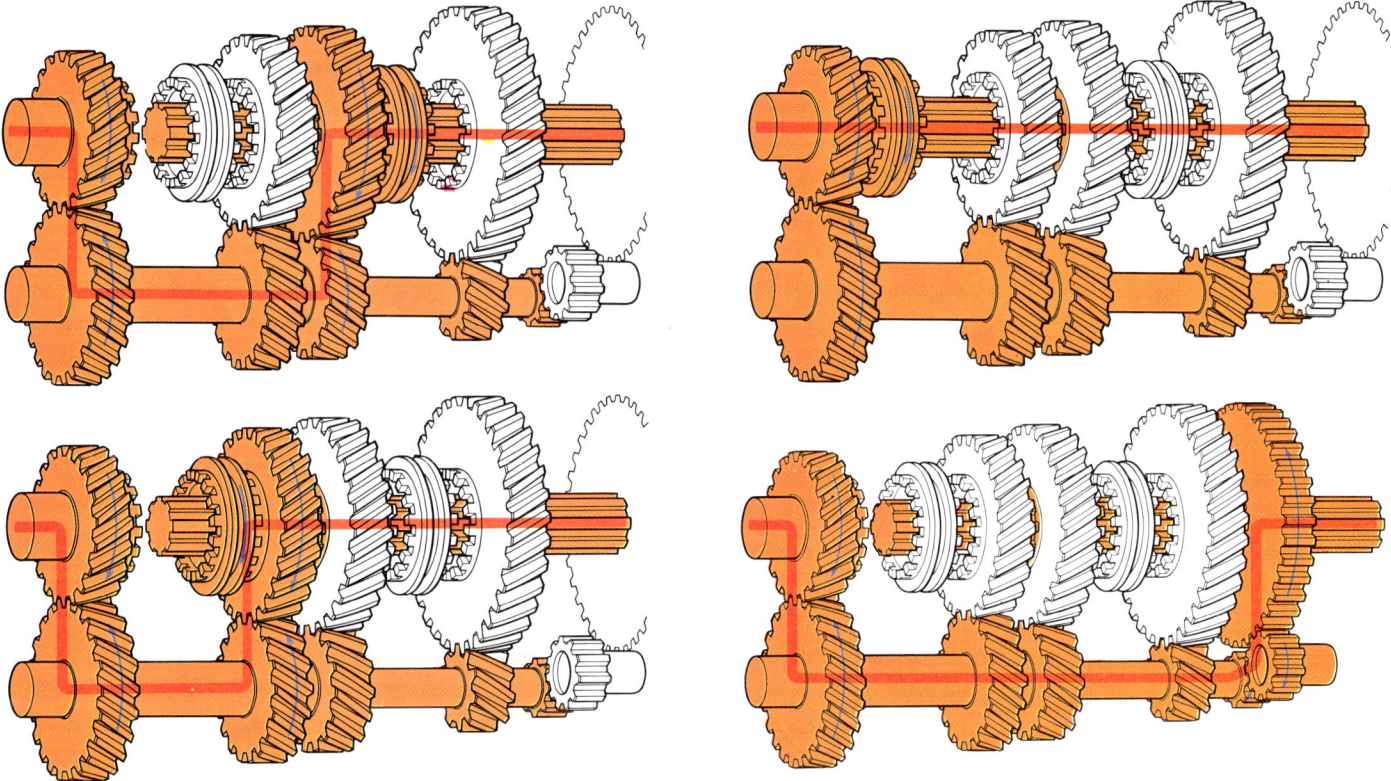

Above: six diagrams showing the power-flow through a four-speed gearbox in neutral *(top left)*, first *(above left)*, second *(top)*, third *(above)*, fourth *(top right)* and reverse *(above right)*

Left: a sectional drawing of the same gearbox, showing how it connects to the clutch

potential customers by driving at a steady 60 mph while slipping freely from one gear to another of the uppermost three. Most customers had never done 60 at all, let alone in second gear!

What made the gearchanging so tricky was the need for the rotational rates of two spur gears to be synchronised before one could be slid axially along its shaft to move sideways into mesh with the other, fixed to another parallel shaft. Then, as now, the majority of manually-operated gearboxes were of the two-shaft layout, the input and output shafts being coaxial and treated as one (the mainshaft) while the parallel shaft (emulating the 'back gear' of lathes and certain other machine tools with which the designers would be familiar) was called the layshaft. This arrangement provided direct drive in top gear, the two portions of the mainshaft being coupled together by a dog clutch—a kind of gearwheel with teeth on its face rather than on its rim—so that the input and output shafts rotated as one. A spur gear on the input shaft was permanently meshed with another fixed to the layshaft (all the layshaft's gears were fixed) but the gearwheels on the output shaft were splined so that, although they must always rotate with it, they were permitted axial movement: in top gear, or in neutral, they were all slid away from the layshaft gears. When a change down from top gear was undertaken, the motions of the gearlever

to the output shaft, and the reduction in gear ratio—or the increase in engine revolutions, which would inversely express the same thing—was the product of the ratio of the first pair of meshing gears multiplied by that of the second pair.

It was often found that the change into top gear was easier than the others, for the facial serrations of the dog clutch did not have to be as precisely formed as the involute teeth of the spur gears, and could be made with a measure of deliberate backlash or sloppiness which greatly eased its engagement. This led to the development of the constant-mesh gearbox, albeit by easy stages which began with the advertisement of a 'silent third' and progressed down through the gears until they were all similar—though it was decades before the sliding-pinion bottom gear was finally ousted, and it is with us still in the reverse gear of most manual boxes. In the constant-mesh box, the gears carried by the output shaft are permanently enmeshed with those of the layshaft, but are carried on bearings which leave them free to rotate idly. The appropriate gearwheel may then be locked to the output shaft and made to revolve with it by a dog clutch splined to the shaft and slid along it by the same sort of selector fork and collar as previously moved the sliding pinions.

This was a great improvement. Not only was the gearchange much sweeter, and the need for synchro-

Gearbox/HOW IT WORKS

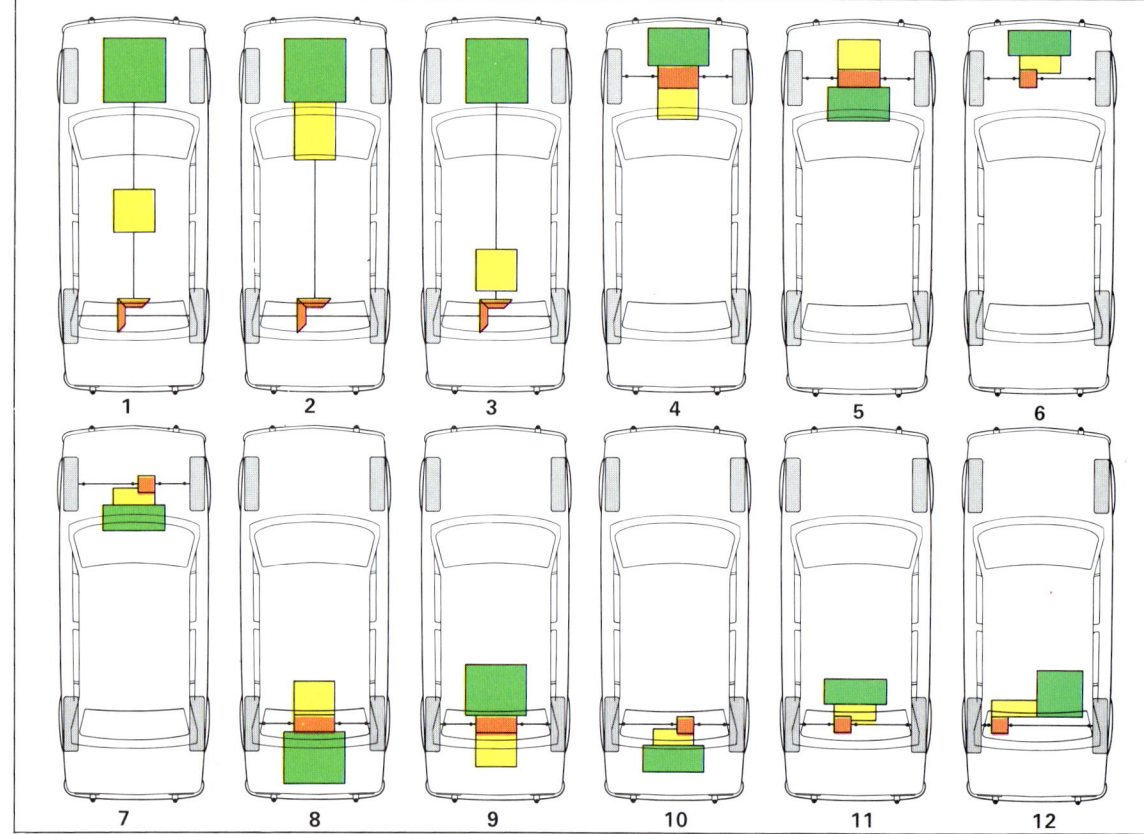

Left: twelve variations of how the gearbox is situated in relation to the engine, differential and axles of a road car.
1 A centrally mounted gearbox, used mainly on veteran and vintage machinery, but also seen on the Morgan Plus Four
2 The most common layout for rear-wheel-drive cars, with the box mated directly to the engine
3 For better weight distribution, the gearbox is mounted in unit with the differential. This layout is used on the Alfetta and Ferrari Daytona
4 The Citroën GS layout, with the engine at the extreme front, allows ample passenger space
5 The rather unusual layout of the Renault 4 and 16 series
6 The famous Issigonis layout, used on the Mini, also gives plenty of passenger room
7 Yet another variation for the front-wheel-drive car, this time on the Peugeot 104
8 This rear-engined layout is of the type used on the various Volkswagen air-cooled models
9 This mid-engined layout is used on all current Formula One cars and also on the De Tomaso Pantera
10 No cars are now built with a transverse rear-mounted engine
11 The layout that is used on the Ferrari Dino 246GT and the Ferrari Boxer
12 A somewhat unusual mid-engined layout, which is employed on the eight-cylinder Lamborghini Urraco

nisation by double-declutching less exacting (indeed it was possible to snatch the lever from one position to the next without any pause at all), but also it was now possible to employ helical-gear teeth which ran far less noisily than the old straight-cut spurs. A gearbox of this kind can be sheer bliss to operate, especially if the ratios are close in the old Henry fashion. Most racing cars and all motor cycles are still thus equipped, and their drivers seldom ask for better.

If the dog clutches could be replaced by some kind of friction clutch, perfect synchronisation of the output shaft and the selected gearwheel could be achieved rapidly and smoothly. A friction clutch strong enough to transmit full torque would be far too big and heavy, but a small clutch that had to do no more than overcome the inertia of a freely rotating gear and layshaft assembly could be quite small. From this reasoning sprang the invention of synchromesh, introduced by General Motors in the 1928 Cadillac: a small all-metal friction clutch is built onto the face of the selector collar, surrounding the dog clutch. When the selector moves the collar towards the chosen gearwheel, the friction clutch engages a conical surface on the face of the gear, and the friction accelerates or decelerates the gear wheel until it matches the rate of rotation of the output shaft. Further movement of the selector collar then pushes the dog clutch through the bore of the friction clutch to engage the corresponding dogs on the face of the gear wheel. This relative movement of the collar and the friction clutch is made possible by spring loading of the sleeve which allows concentric assembly of the two.

Synchromesh rapidly assumed widespread and deserved popularity. Early versions were soon improved, one of the first amendments being to reverse the positions of the dogs and the cones so that the former were outside the latter and endured less severe stresses when subjected to full torque. Various baulking systems, which made it impossible for the dogs to engage before perfect synchronism had been achieved by the clutch cones, followed; the best known are the Warner and the Porsche systems but, although different systems give different feel or feedback through the gearlever when the baulking mechanism is at work, the effect is similar in all cases.

Even with all these refinements, gearchanging still called for some modest skill and co-ordination on the part of the driver. At the same time, many engineers felt that the crudeness of the conventional gearbox (in which the forces involved tend to bend the shafts, distort the bearings, and tear the casing apart) was an affront to mechanical propriety. While the infinitely or steplessly variable transmission remained an unattainable ideal for decades, it was known that a discrete number of suitable ratios could be obtained from trains of epicyclic gears: the teeth of these are always enmeshed, and their disposition leaves ample room for friction clutches of generous size to control the locking and unlocking of the armatures and rings carrying the gears. First and simplest of these epicyclic transmissions was the two-speed (and reverse) gearbox of the Ford T, which went into production twenty years before the appearance of synchromesh. Many drivers knew no other way of changing gear but the curious pedalling tricks by which the Model T was controlled; however, the wider performance range of later and more sophisticated cars demanded more speeds.

By the time that synchromesh was well established, an elegant epicyclic alternative was available in a few cars. This was the four-speed Wilson preselective self-changing gearbox, the precursor of nearly all the automatic transmissions in use today. In it was a series of four coaxial epicyclic gear trains, the annulus of each presenting a smooth cylindrical exterior upon which a band brake could operate to clamp the annulus (or ring gear) and stop it moving. According to the brake selected, any one of the lowest three speeds or reverse would be secured; and the progres-

HOW IT WORKS/Gearbox

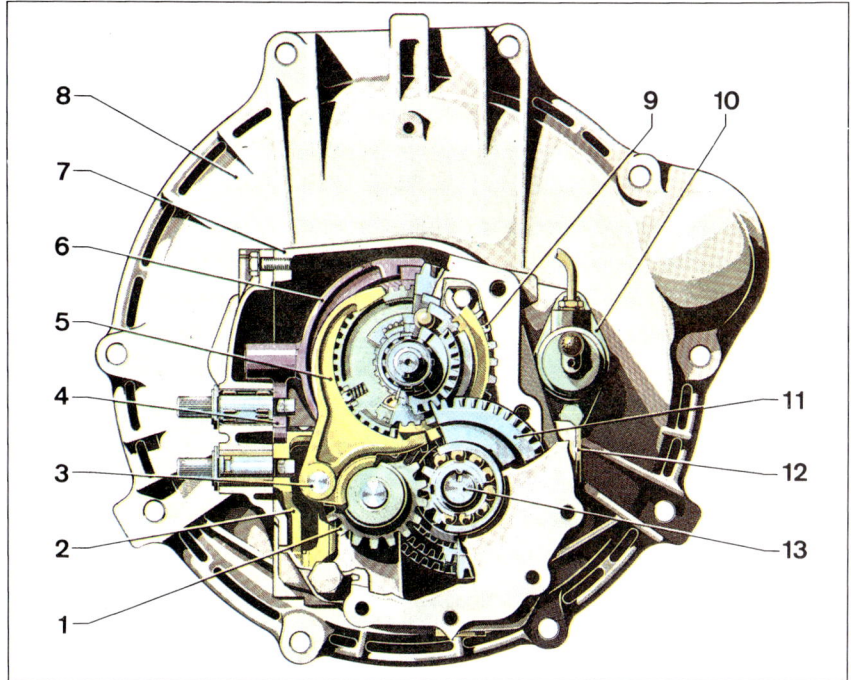

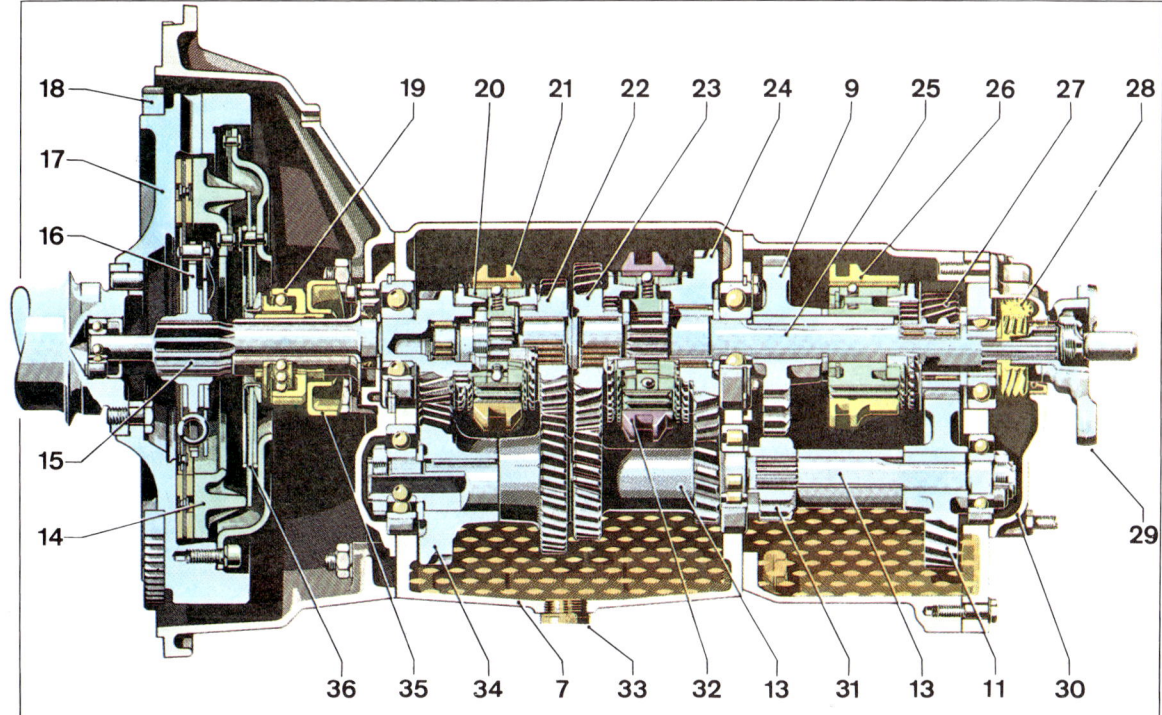

Above and right: two cutaway drawings of the five-speed manual gearbox used on the Mercedes 230, 250, 280 and 300 series.
1 = 1st, 2 = 2nd, 3 = 3rd, 4 = 4th, 5 = 5th and R = reverse
1 Reverse Gear
2 Shift ring 5 & R
3 Shift rod 5 & R
4 Shift detent 1 & 2
5 Shift fork 5 & R
6 Shift fork 1 & 2
7 Transmission case
8 Clutch housing
9 Reverse mainshaft
10 Slave cylinder
11 Helical gear 5
12 Oil filter plug
13 Countershaft
14 Clutch pressure plate
15 Drive shaft
16 Clutch plate
17 Flywheel
18 Starter ring gear
19 Release bearing
20 Synchroniser ring 4
21 Sliding sleeve 3 & 4
22 Helical gear 3
23 Helical gear 2
24 Helical gear 1
25 Main shaft
26 Sliding sleeve 5
27 Helical gear 5
28 Speedometer drive
29 Three-arm flange
30 Transmission cover
31 R gear countershaft
32 Sliding sleeve 1 & 2
33 Oil drain plug
34 Countershaft gear
35 Release member
36 Diaphragm spring

The driver could change his mind at any time and move the lever to another position, except when actually releasing the pedal. In the Talbot car, designer Roesch arranged that gearchanges would take place in an automatic sequence leading up to and down from top gear unless the driver interfered but, in the 1930s, there was no demand for such refinements: drivers were happy enough that they could enjoy anything from a leisurely change to a racing snap without any skill or doubt. Touring cars such as the Daimler and Armstrong Siddeley had a fluid coupling interposed between engine and gearbox, to give ineffable smoothness of take-off and to cushion each change, although this impaired the high mechanical efficiency of the Wilson box. Sporting saloons such as the Riley sometimes had instead a centrifugally-operated friction clutch, sometimes called the traffic clutch, which allowed the engine to idle in gear. Racing cars such as the ERA did without a separate clutch and relied on the brake band controlling bottom gear to provide the necessary progression of grip when starting.

The Wilson gearbox was almost entirely confined to British cars, and remained in production until the demise of the Armstrong Siddeley. Shorter lived but more refined was the French Cotal gearbox: it had fewer trains and hence a less attractive progression of

sive operation of the brake, by spring-loaded toggles, ensured positive and shock-free take-up of the drive, quietly and as quickly or slowly as the driver wished. Each band brake constituted a clutch and could be used as such, but the clutch pedal also operated the selector linkages to engage whichever speed the driver had determined in advance to use by moving a lever to the appropriate notch of a quadrant. When he 'preselected' top gear, the corresponding toggle would be cocked, and when next he fully depressed and released the clutch pedal the selector mechanism would be triggered as for the other speeds; but in the case of top gear, all the band brakes would be freed, while a cone clutch at one end of the series of gear trains locked the whole lot together so that they rotated as one unit to give direct drive from the input shaft to the output shaft.

ratios, but instead of the gruesome mechanical linkages characteristic of the British design it rejoiced in electromagnetic control of the gears, under the fingertip direction of a tiny gearlever (looking like a cherry on a cocktail stick) moving in a miniature gate.

It was General Motors in America that gave the epicyclic gearbox mass appeal. In 1937, the Buick and Oldsmobile were marketed with a semi-automatic transmission in which all gearchanges were arranged to occur whenever the prevailing combination of vehicle speed and engine speed and load dictated. The system was semi-automatic only inasmuch as a conventional clutch still had to be worked by the driver when starting and stopping; two years later they had productionised the fluid coupling and the fully automatic Hydra-Matic transmission was born. Although the hydrokinetic couplings associated with conven-

759

tional automatic transmissions have been the subject of endless experiment and change in the ensuing years, practically all automatic gearboxes have been essentially similar to this GM design, making use of two or three epicyclic trains to give three or four speeds forward and the usual one in reverse.

The notable change from the early Wilson and Cotal boxes has been in the means used to control the gear trains. Not only the annuli but also the planet carriers may be held fast, enabling a greater number of speeds to be offered by an epicyclic train and thus saving the cost of manufacturing gears. The old contracting band brakes are supplemented by multi-plate clutches coaxial with the gearshaft, and the operation of these is usually by high-pressure oil from a pump built into the gearbox. In the bottom of the gearbox casing is an elaborate hydraulic circuit embodying valves which direct the oil pressure in varying ways, according to the demands conveyed by connections with the engine throttle and inlet manifold vacuum and the driver's control lever. Such hydraulic systems are not an essential feature of the automatic gearbox; in the Renault version, for instance, the brakes and clutches are applied by solenoids controlled by electronic circuitry.

Even the epicyclic gear train is not inviolate. The Automotive Products transmission, employed by British Leyland in some of their front-wheel-drive cars such as the Mini, substitutes bevel-gear differentials for some of the usual spur-gear sets, and incorporates a sprag-clutch or freewheel in bottom gear, as do some others.

One of the most commendably neat automatic gearboxes was the now defunct Hobbs Mechamatic, which saw effective service in everything from delivery vans to a special racing Lotus Elite. In this, one single epicyclic-gear train of compound construction (three coaxial sun gears, one planet carrier and no annulus) gave four forward speeds and one reverse under the control of two plate clutches and three disc brakes, all operated by hydraulic pressure behind diaphragms.

While on the subject of exceptions to generality, some variations in the layout of manually operated gearboxes should be noted. Not all such boxes offer direct drive in top gear, for instance, although it is often held desirable that they should: this is because mechanical losses are negligible in direct drive, whereas in the other speeds (supposedly less used) there is a penalty of about 4%. Other engineers insist that it is better to have an all-indirect gearbox in which the drive passes from the mainshaft to the layshaft through one pair of spur gears in each speed, so that power losses are about 2% in each case. In practice, all-indirect boxes are popular for rear-engined and front-wheel-drive cars, since the layout enables the output to emerge from the same end of the gearbox housing as the input entered. In the past there have been cars (particularly in Edwardian times) of conventional layout but with direct drive in third gear, top being then an 'overdrive' in the sense that the output rpm will be higher than the input rpm. This is not a good definition of overdrive, which should be related to the car's matching of tractive effort against resistance in the gear concerned, but the usage is prevalent and should be noted.

The balance of tractive effort and resistance is what should determine the ratios of each gear and the number to be made available. In brief, it may be said that the lowest gear ratio offered need be no lower than is necessary for a start to be made on the steepest gradient envisaged, nor any lower than would multiply the torque to the point where tractive effort would

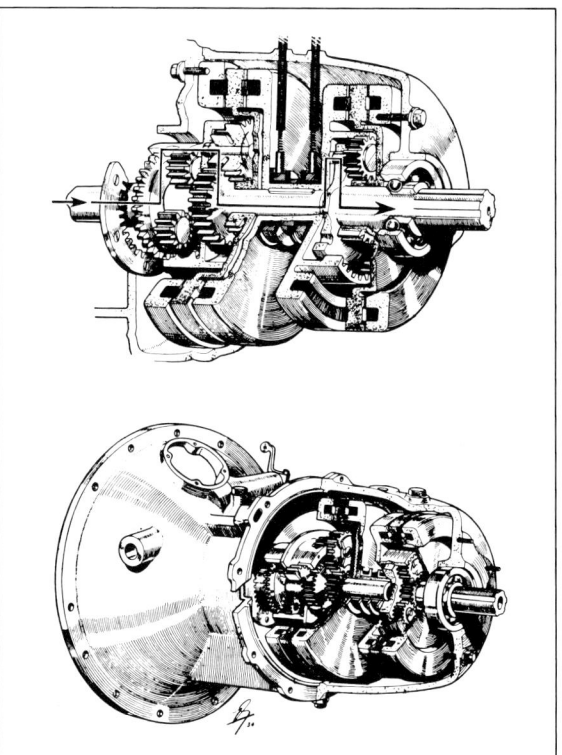

Left: two cutaway drawings of the French Cotal electro-magnetic pre-selector gearbox. This French design was similar to the British Wilson box but, instead of having cumbersome mechanical linkages, the Cotal box was operated electro-magnetically by a delicate gear lever. This gearbox was used in the nineteen thirties, but never saw great success

appreciably exceed the tractive capacity of the tyres; and, of course, it must be no lower than the maximum permissible stresses that the transmission can allow.

Top gear may be chosen according to any of a number of design considerations; but how many others should be offered between top and bottom, and what their spacing should be, will depend on the shape of the engine's full-throttle torque curve and the size of the production budget. An engine that is big and flexible, with lots of back-up torque and high-speed asthma, may call for no more than three speeds. A small engine, or one with a torque curve rising to a peak at or near the peak-power speed (they rarely coincide) may need five or six.

Geographical influences are evident in gearboxes, too. Italy, a country of many hills and some long flat roads, used to go in for three quite closely-spaced low gears and a remote high top gear. Germany, with everything from Alps to Autobahns, also favoured a high top and a low bottom, but with the intermediate ratios evenly spaced. The English used to be congenital top-gear staggerers, but had no mountains worthy of the name, so their top gear was rather low; the next was close to it because that was the only other gear in frequent use and an easy change was demanded, and any others were calculated to serve the unlikely eventuality that the driver would dare to attempt one of the more famous hills such as Porlock, Sutton Bank or Wrynose. As for the Americans, they always had such big engines that they could go everywhere in top anyway, and they soon forgot how to change gear. The automatic transmission certainly helped them to forget; but nowadays, when the pressures of international marketing have constrained all cars to be more alike than in the past, the very processes of memory and oblivion are obscured. The Grand Prix racer and the heavy truck perpetuate Panhard's *fin du siècle* brutalities (although most heavy trucks now have synchromesh and some have semi-automatic gearboxes), while everything else apes General Motors. Whether this is something to be remembered or forgotten should perhaps be left to the reader. LJKS

BETTER DRIVING/Gearchanging

MAKING PROPER USE OF THE GEARBOX

There is very little skill required to change gear in the modern motor car. To use the gearbox skilfully, however, is a completely different matter

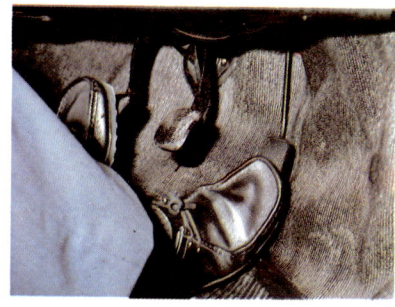 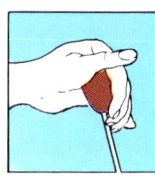

The sequence for double-de-clutching (from 4th to 3rd) is as follows. The gear lever is shown, right, in 4th gear. The driver's left foot is over the clutch ready to depress it, while the right foot is about to lift off the accelerator

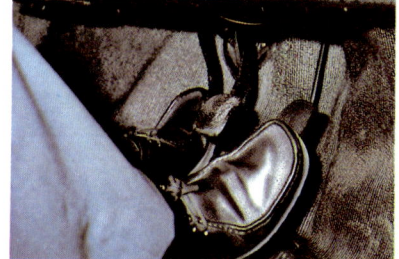 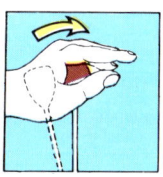

The right foot is now clear of the accelerator and the left foot depresses the clutch. While so doing, the hand, already positioned on the gear lever, moves forward, putting the lever in neutral

 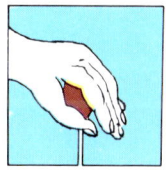

The left foot is now off the clutch and the gear lever is in neutral. The right foot now 'blips' the accelerator to approximately half of the full travel, so that when third gear is engaged, the engine and gear speeds are synchronised

After blipping the accelerator, the right foot is lifted clear of the pedal and the clutch depressed again. When the clutch pedal reaches the end of its travel, the gear lever is moved forward from neutral into third

 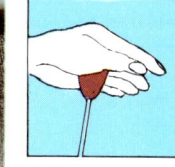

Finally, with the lever in third, the clutch is engaged progressively, to ensure a smooth take-up of drive. When first practised, the procedure may be less than smooth. However, experience will ensure perfection

VERY LITTLE SKILL IS REQUIRED in changing gear on a modern car fitted with a synchromesh gearbox, for anyone who is capable of depressing a foot pedal and pushing a lever around can successfully change gear. To use a gearbox skilfully is another matter entirely.

A gearbox of some sort is necessary on a car because no internal-combustion engine has sufficient power or torque to cope with all the demands of road speed, gradient etc, without having some means of keeping the engine working at its most efficient speed. The driver also requires some means of disconnecting the drive when it is necessary to stop, and some form of gearing is required in order to reverse the car.

In the early days of motoring and, indeed, until the 1930s, car gearboxes were generally provided with no means of synchronising the gears as they meshed, so that great skill was needed to select a gear noiselessly, especially when changing down through the gears. In fact, so demanding were some gearboxes that they would refuse to engage a gear unless the gear speeds were perfectly synchronised; the driver would be reminded of his clumsiness by a fearsome grating noise from the gearbox and very often with smarting knuckles as the gear lever whipped out of engagement.

By the 1930s, gearboxes were often fitted with synchromesh on some of the ratios but first and reverse were seldom supplied with synchromesh, and indeed it is only in recent years that the vast majority of cars have been fitted with synchromesh on first gear. Reverse gear is not usually fitted with synchromesh because it is only engaged when the car is at rest. There are various types of synchromesh, but they all work on the principle of equalising the speeds of two gears which are required to mesh with each other before allowing the teeth to engage.

This method of gearchanging is virtually foolproof except on the few cars which have exceptionally poor gearbox designs, or when the synchromesh has worn so badly that it is ineffective.

Drivers soon learn how and when to change gear when they are under instruction, and it soon becomes almost second nature to the vast majority of drivers. The sound of the engine is the most appropriate signal to the driver for, if the engine reaches the upper end of its revolution range, acceleration begins to tail off and it is time to change into the next higher gear. Likewise, if the engine begins to labour when climbing a hill, then it is time to change down to prevent the engine stalling. The learner quickly discovers how to do this, but few bother to progress beyond the stage of depressing the clutch pedal and moving the gear lever in the required direction.

Despite the use of synchromesh, there is still scope for the good driver to demonstrate his or her skill in the use of the clutch and gearbox. The clutch is quite a delicate mechanism, and a clumsy driver can wear one out in 15,000 miles, so a feather-light touch on the clutch pedal will be more than repaid in extra clutch

Gearchanging/BETTER DRIVING

life. The clutch should always be allowed to engage smoothly and progressively so that the car moves away without jerking; this requires the driver to use just the right amount of engine revolutions as the clutch engages—too many and the car will jerk or the clutch will slip; too few and the car may well stall or hop away from rest in an untidy way. A driver who allows the clutch to judder frequently will find that the clutch plates become ridged, causing severe vibrations through the transmission.

Keen drivers tend to change gear as quickly as possible, depressing the clutch pedal only far enough to free the plates, then whipping the gear lever rapidly from gear to gear. With a good synchromesh gearbox, this causes no problems, although it will tend to accelerate wear on the synchromesh cones, but on cars with a poor design of synchromesh or a worn gearbox, this will cause a good deal of noise and, again, it will accelerate wear. Some cars have particularly obtrusive synchromesh which refuses to be 'rushed'—in other words, if the driver attempts to change gear rapidly, the synchromesh prevents a rapid change, and may even prevent the gear being engaged at all. Sometimes, this tendency disappears after the gearbox has covered a few thousand miles.

Many drivers use the gearbox as a means of braking the car. Instead of using the brakes to slow from say 70 mph to 50 mph to take a corner, they may change down from top to third gear and allow the engine compression to slow the car with the throttle pedal released. When the speed is low enough, they then accelerate through the bend. This method of braking is frowned on in official circles, mainly because of the inherent danger of the gear not engaging properly or the driver missing the gear and finding neutral; it may then be too late to apply the brakes. This problem can be overcome by using the heel-and-toe method of braking and gear changing. This method is used almost all the time by racing and rally drivers who need to brake at the latest possible time in order to negotiate a corner as rapidly as possible. Obviously, if a driver has to brake to his correct cornering speed and then change gear, he is losing time on the driver who is braking and changing gear at the same time.

The techniques used in heel-and-toe gear changing vary from driver to driver and from car to car. Some cars have the brake and accelerator pedals well placed for heel-and-toe changes, while others have very badly positioned pedals. Depending on the position of the pedals and the driver's preferences, there are two different methods of heel-and-toe braking and gear changing. One is to brake with the toe part of the foot, angling the heel outwards to work the accelerator pedal, while the other is to brake with the left side of your foot, and use the right side to operate the accelerator. The technique is usually combined with double de-clutching which was an essential before synchromesh became available, but is now rarely used except by racing drivers whose cars are not fitted with synchromesh gearboxes. However, it can be useful on cars which do not have synchromesh on first gear as double de-clutching does allow the gear to be engaged while the car is moving and also prevents grating of the gears as they are engaged.

The full double-de-clutching routine for a downward change combined with heel-and-toe braking goes as follows: place the toe of the right foot on the brake pedal and begin braking, at the same time depressing the clutch with the left foot and moving the gear lever into neutral. Now release the clutch pedal and flick the accelerator pedal with the heel of the right foot so that engine revs rise briefly, then fall

again. Now press the clutch pedal to the floor again and move the gear lever into the appropriate gear, at the same time removing the right toe from the brake and transferring the right foot back to the accelerator pedal. This method sounds rather clumsy and time consuming, but the skilled driver can double de-clutch, brake and change down in little more than one second.

It is necessary to de-clutch twice and blip the accelerator pedal in order to equalise the speed of the two gears which are to engage. By blipping the throttle, the driver speeds up the gear on the gearbox primary shaft to the same speed as that of the lower gear. Some practice will be required to perfect this technique as only several attempts will show the driver exactly how hard he must blip the accelerator pedal to achieve the correct gear speeds.

It is obviously important not to change down to a lower gear at a speed which is too high for that gear. A tachometer or rev counter is an important aid in preventing this because the driver can see the exact rev drop between each gear on the dial. If, for instance, the driver changes from third gear at his maximum permitted revs of 6000 rpm into top gear and the revs drop to 4000 rpm, the rev drop between third and top is 2000 rpm. The driver then knows that he must not change down into third gear when travelling at more than 4000 rpm in top gear, otherwise the engine will be over-revved when he changes down. This task is assisted on some cars which have gear speeds marked on the speedometer, although these are usually somewhat conservative figures well below the maximum permitted engine revolutions. MT

Above: the double-de-clutching technique may be used to change down at any time—especially if the synchromesh is weak—so that the driver can be in the correct gear all the time, for accelerating or braking. If retardation higher than can be achieved with engine compression alone is needed, the double-de-clutching technique can be taken one stage further: heel-and-toeing. Basically, the normal procedure is followed, with the difference that during all of the sequences, smooth and progressive braking must be achieved by using the ball of the right foot on the brake pedal while the heel of the foot controls the accelerator. It is also possible to use the left side of the foot to brake, while using the right to 'blip' the throttle

THE MOTOR INDUSTRY/**General Motors**

AN INDUSTRIAL GIANT

Founded in 1908, General Motors is reputedly the largest company in the world. The man who started it all was an entrepreneur named William C. Durant

Above: the massive General Motors building on Broadway, New York

Richard C. Gorstenberg, the Chairman of the General Motors Corporation in 1974

IT IS AN INTRIGUING THOUGHT that the biggest automotive company in the world might never have happened had David Dunbar Buick stuck to making bathtubs and U-bends for a living, instead of trying to make money out of the horseless carriage. For, in less than a year, the Buick company, founded in 1903, had become an utter financial failure, and the worried investors were seeking a miracle man who could pull the seemingly doomed company back on to a profitable basis. Their choice was a 44-year-old Michigan carriage builder, who had little idea of how a car was built and even less of what made it run; it was an inspired decision.

The man they selected, William Crapo Durant, was one of that select group of natural entrepreneurs who were to transform America from an agricultural to an industrial nation. Durant, who was born in 1860, came from a family whose fortunes were large enough for him to have lived a life of idleness had he so wished, but young Billy had all the right 'go-getting' instincts and started out to make his own career when he was sixteen years old.

By the turn of the century, Billy Durant had become the head of the biggest cart and carriage makers in Flint, Michigan, America's carriage capital, in partnership with one J. Dallas Dort. He was a natural salesman, and proved it when he took over Buick by selling $500,000 of company stock in a day.

Within three years, the Buick company had an annual production of over 8000 cars in its new home in Flint, and was one of the big four of the infant American motor industry. Durant, however, had bigger ideas still. He felt that the individual motor company offering a single model line was at the mercy of the buying public and, if they failed to buy sufficient of its products in a given year, that could spell disaster. He reasoned that a consortium of major producers could support each other in times of crisis, as well as organising their own parts-manufacturing companies to ensure that they always had an adequate supply of the right components in the right place at the right time, and at the right price.

So Billy called a meeting of the four leading manufacturers—himself, Benjamin Briscoe of Maxwell-Briscoe, Ransome Eli Olds of Reo, and Henry Ford. It looked as though Durant's proposals for a merger between the four companies was well on the way to fruition when Henry Ford suddenly scuppered the scheme by asking for the $3 million agreed value of the Ford Motor Company in cash; this triggered Olds to ask for payments in gold, too. Of course, Durant, who had envisaged the merger as a gentlemanly exchange of share certificates, could not raise $6 million in real money, and the deal was off.

There was, apparently, a second attempt to buy Ford in 1909 but, by then, the price had risen to $8 million cash, even further out of Durant's reach.

However, Billy had already decided that he could

achieve his dream of dominating the American motor industry without the help of the other big four companies, and by 1908 he had floated the General Motors Corporation of New Jersey, which absorbed Buick by an exchange of stock. It was the first step in a breathtaking essay at empire-building.

Next, Durant took over the ailing Oldsmobile company, once the biggest of America's car makers, whose sales had plummeted from 6500 in 1905 to 1055 in 1908; then he acquired the Oakland Motor Company, founded less than two years previously. There followed, with bewildering rapidity, the takeover of a further twenty companies, including Elmore, Rainier, Rapid Cartercar, Welch, Reliance, Randolph, Welch-Detroit and Cadillac. That bearded patriarch, Walter Leland, of Cadillac had no intention of trading his company for a mass of share certificates and, like Ford, insisted on cash. The price was $3.5 million, and Durant was given ten days to raise it. When he returned, six months later, the price was up to $4,125,000; by the time the sale had gone through, Cadillac cost $4.5 million.

Durant's madcap spending spree, acquiring companies for their availability rather than their earning potential, could have only one end—it came in 1910. The gold-plated straw that broke the corporate camel's back was the Heany electric lamp company, acquired for $7,131,259 (although only $112,759 of this was in cash) on the basis that Heany owned the basic patent covering tungsten-filament lamps, which were then being mooted as a replacement for oil and acetylene lighting. A costly law suit proved otherwise and, although General Motors as a whole had just made a net profit of $10 million, and produced one-fifth of all American cars, the Heany venture killed their chances of raising the much-needed capital. No bank would risk lending money to a man who had just squandered $7 million on a worthless patent, and General Motors needed $12 million to keep in business.

When Durant finally found a bankers' syndicate who would bail him out, the terms were crippling. The syndicate, headed by James J. Storrow, of Lee, Higginson & Company, was prepared to loan General Motors $15 million at six per cent. However, they took $2.5 million of this back as commission, as well as $6 million in General Motors stock. Durant, of course, was removed from control (although he remained on the board); in 1910, unable to stomach his loss in status, Durant resigned.

Having bailed out the General Motors Group, the bankers set about making it profitable. At first they thought of axing everything but the two most profitable companies, Buick and Cadillac, but Henry Leland persuaded them to keep the group alive. Even so, there were rationalisations—Rainier and Welch were amalgamated in 1911, to produce a car called the Marquette, which survived only a year, while Cartercar ceased production in 1916 (although its associate company, Pontiac, was revived later).

Left: the five-lane 'endless motorway' at Vauxhall's test ground in Millbrook, Bedfordshire

Above left: one of the GM cars that has won acclaim in both America and Europe, the Pontiac Firebird Trans-Am

Above: an aerial view of the Vauxhall test track. Built on a 700-acre site, the complex cost 3½ million pounds

General Motors/THE MOTOR INDUSTRY

The Storrow syndicate put in its own nominees at the head of General Motors: Charles W. Nash became president in 1912, while Walter P. Chrysler became works manager. Both men were to make a major impact on the industry in later years as the heads of their own companies. Under their guidance, General Motors made a steady recovery, but they had not heard the last of the indefatigable Billy Durant, the 'Man with the midas touch'.

Durant had returned to Flint, and established the Little Motor Car Company on a capital outlay of $26,000, selling 3500 cars in the first year. Then he launched Chevrolet, which combined with Little in 1913; the success of the Chevrolet launch enabled Durant to seek capitalisation from the rich DuPont banking family. A new company, Chevrolet Motors of Delaware, was incorporated for $20 million—later raised to $80 million—to absorb the old Chevrolet company. Then Durant offered to exchange five shares in Chevrolet for one share of General Motors; the investors responded eagerly. In addition, Durant and DuPont bought up any shares in General Motors which came onto the market. Thus it was, that in 1915 Billy Durant could walk back into General Motors and say: 'Gentlemen, I control this company!'

Nash, who did not share Durant's ebullient vision of the future prospects of the motor industry, resigned; backed by Storrow, he founded the Nash Motor Company, aiming at the more conservative sector of the market.

At first, 'Durant's Second Empire' was based on the organisational nonsense that the part was greater than the whole, that Chevrolet, one of the manufacturing companies making up the General Motors organisation, actually owned the parent company. This situation, however, was remedied in 1918 when the General Motors Corporation was created to absorb General

Left: another of GM's New York buildings. This one is situated on Fifth Avenue. General Motors is the biggest company in the world and markets many different items, ranging from refrigerators to luxury Cadillac cars

Below: one of the names synonymous with General Motors is that of Chevrolet; the car pictured is one of their large range—the Caprice Station Wagon

THE MOTOR INDUSTRY/General Motors

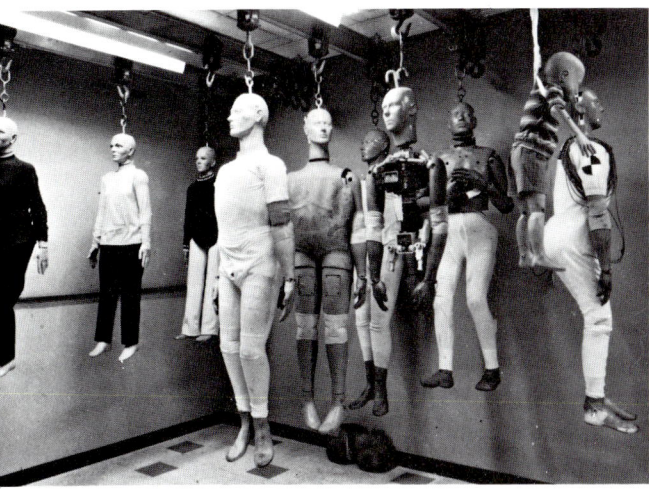

Left above: all part of the GM family. These dummies, made of plastic skin over a skeleton of steel, aluminium and bronze, cost £5000 each. They are used on an impact simulator

Left below: a Vauxhall Victor prototype being crash tested into a 75-ton concrete block

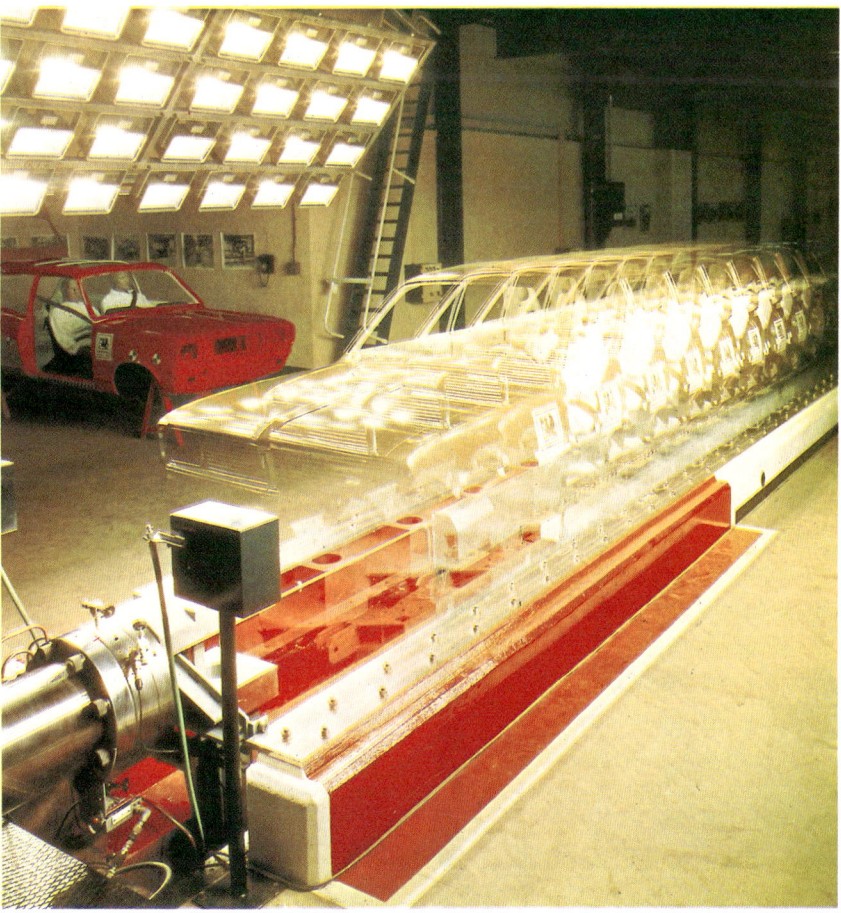

Below: a multi-sequence photograph of a Vauxhall Viva on the impact simulator at the Millbrook test ground in Bedfordshire, England

Motors Company and Chevrolet, as well as another of Durant's creations, a consortium of parts manufacturers called the United Motors Corporation, which linked such companies as Delco and the Hyatt Roller Bearing Company. It was a move which was to ensure the future growth of the General Motors Corporation, had Billy Durant realised it, for it brought into the company two men who were to play a vital part in shaping the organisation. They were Charles F. Kettering, of Delco, a brilliant research scientist who had perfected the electric starter (he was also a pioneer aviator who had helped the Wright brothers build their power unit) and, more importantly, Alfred P. Sloan, of Hyatt.

The Hyatt company had been founded by John Wesley Hyatt, who had invented celluloid as a substitute for ivory, so that billiard balls could be made more cheaply, and had then turned his attention to the design of tapered roller bearings. Sloan had joined Hyatt on graduating from the Massachusetts Institute of Technology, but Hyatt proved to be a far better inventor than businessman, and the company was soon in trouble.

Sloan's father stepped in with a loan of $5000, which saved the company, and his son took over from Hyatt as president. He acquired control at just the right time, for the motor industry was just beginning to expand, and there was an ever-growing demand for Hyatt roller bearings, which Sloan was ready to supply. In time, he had built up the Hyatt company to the point where he felt it had become too big to remain independent. Yet when Billy Durant suggested that Hyatt became part of United Motors, Sloan's initial reaction was one of reluctance. Then he reflected on the fact that he depended on orders from Ford and General Motors for the continued existence of his company: should they decide to make their own bearings, he would be out of business. It would be far better to throw in his lot with one of the two giants while he had the chance. So, Sloan joined United Motors and, when the General Motors Corporation was created in 1918, he became a GM vice-president.

As for Billy Durant, he was back in his element; almost immediately he set about a vast expansion programme. The Chevrolet, Buick and Oldsmobile factories were extended, a completely new Cadillac plant was built, while a new headquarters building rose 15 storeys high above Detroit, where General Motors also opened a new research laboratory. Inevitably, there were many more company acquisitions, as if to compensate for the closures under the James J. Storrow régime.

For $30 million, Durant acquired the Fisher Body Company which, for once, was an acquisition well worth what General Motors had paid for it; indeed, it has been said that if there had been no Fisher Body, there could have been no General Motors as it is known today.

The Fisher family had been engaged in the blacksmith and carriage-building industries for at least two generations when Fred Fisher came to Detroit in 1902, and found a job as a designer with a pioneer car-body manufacturer. Once he was established, he sent for his brother, Charles; then they asked William to join them. Eventually, the remaining four brothers—Edward, Lawrence, Alfred and Howard—were working in Detroit. Inevitably, they combined to form their own body-building company, in 1908. The Fisher Body Company was followed two years later by the Fisher Closed Body Company, and the two were then merged in 1916 to form the Fisher Body Corporation. All seven brothers stayed on after the 1918 takeover.

Above: an experimental GMC coach, due to be put into production in late 1975. Code-named the RTX (Rapid Transport Experimental), the coach has many novel features, including air-cooled front brakes, oil-cooled rear brakes, roof escape hatches, automatic transmission and a suspension system that enables the bus to 'kneel' five inches lower so that passengers can alight safely. The coach will initially be available with a diesel engine, although a gas-turbine unit is also planned

Another of Durant's acquisitions was an unsuccessful one-man operation, the Guardian Frigerator Company, run by Alfred Mellowes, who had built a refrigerator in Dayton, Ohio, in 1915, moved to Detroit to market his invention, and sold just 40 electric freezers in two years, losing $34,000 in the process. Durant bought the company for just $56,300, using his own cash for the purchase, and changed its name to Frigidaire; in 1919, he sold the company to General Motors for what it had cost him.

'What is an automobile manufacturing group doing manufacturing electric refrigerators?' queried his fellow directors.

'That is easy,' countered Billy. 'A refrigerator is really very similar to an automobile—they are both boxes with motors inside!'

GM broke into the finance field with the formation of the General Motors Acceptance Corporation, which provided hopeful customers with the necessary credit to finance the purchase of their new car.

However, the good wrought by such innovations was completely nullified by a mistake of typical Durant proportions. Inspired, no doubt, by the success of the Fordson tractor, Durant persuaded General Motors to build a range of tractors and farm equipment. Walter Chrysler, then heading Buick, warned against such a venture, but was overruled. Time was to prove him right for, in 1920, GM closed this agricultural side of their corporate business, having lost $30,000 in a very short space of time.

Had the post-war boom in car sales continued, Durant's wild spending might have paid off. As it was, the market suddenly collapsed in the mid-1920s, with disastrous results. Durant had tried to control the affairs of all the conglomerate companies of General Motors personally but, as he devoted most of his time to playing the stock market—he is reputed to have operated at least 70 different brokerage accounts—and either ignored his subordinates completely or else unnecessarily interfered with the way they were carrying out their work, the affairs of the GM corporation were slipping rapidly from his grasp.

Chrysler left in disgust over the tractor episode in mid-1920 while Sloan, equally frustrated, but not ready to resign, worked out a reorganisation plan which he presented to Durant. Billy approved the plan—but did not do anything about it.

Sloan realised that Durant was beyond help, and took a trip to Europe to consider what to do next. He decided to resign as soon as he got back to Detroit. But nemesis had already overtaken Durant, whose personal finances were heavily overcommitted, and who had been trying an impossible juggling trick to keep General Motors in business, for the corporation's stock had plunged from $400 to $12 a share. Durant pumped $90 million into the market in a desperate bid to raise share prices, but without success. When Pierre S. DuPont heard that Durant was threatened with

THE MOTOR INDUSTRY/General Motors

Above: an artist's impression of the 4-rotor, 6.4-litre Wankel Corvette. The car features a glassfibre body, as have all Chevrolet Corvettes

bankruptcy, he acted immediately and found that Billy's finances were so tangled that he just did not know where he stood. DuPont and the Morgan banking interests united to save General Motors, and bought out Durant, who held 2,500,000 shares in the corporation, on condition that he resigned.

DuPont, reluctantly, became president, but he was just a figurehead to inspire confidence in the corporation's renewed financial stability. The power now lay with Alfred P. Sloan, the new executive vice-president.

'General Motors had become too big to be a one-man show,' commented Sloan. 'It was already far too complicated. The future required more than an individual's genius.' 'Dictatorship,' he added, 'is the most effective way of administration, provided the dictators know the complete answer to all questions. But he never does—and never will.'

In place of Durant's erratic dictatorship, Sloan proposed that, while the corporation should follow a co-ordinated central policy, each of the component companies should operate as autonomous units within that framework. And he was ready to buy the finest talent available to ensure the new régime's success.

A prime opportunity came early in 1921, when William S. Knudsen, one of the top men in the Ford Motor Company, was discharged, apparently for showing too much independence and thus treading on the toes of his fellow-Dane, Charles Sorensen, Henry Ford's right-hand man. For a while, Knudsen managed a Detroit car accessory factory, and then he happened to meet Sloan. There was, in fact, no job available at General Motors for a man of Knudsen's qualifications, but Sloan at once offered him a place on the corporation's general staff. Within just a month, Knudsen had become vice-president in charge of the Chevrolet division.

In fact, Chevrolet sales had slumped so badly since World War I, that DuPont had considered abandoning it altogether: from 144,500 cars in 1920, Chevrolet sales had fallen to 75,700 the next year, and the result was a loss of $8.7 million. A group of consulting engineers reported that Chevrolet was no longer competitive, and should be liquidated, but Sloan thought that with lower prices and better salesmanship and engineering, the marque still stood a chance of breaking into the mass market, and he convinced DuPont to override the engineers' report.

Under Knudsen's inspired leadership, Chevrolet expanded rapidly; when he took over, in 1922, Ford was outselling Chevrolet 13 to 1. Only seven years later, Chevrolet became America's best-selling car.

Another ex-Ford man snapped up by GM was

General Motors / THE MOTOR INDUSTRY

Norval A. Hawkins who, at a reputed salary of $150,000 a year, reorganised the various companies in the corporation so that their products should not compete with one another, reclassifying the marques into their own distinctive price and style categories, and improving General Motors' financial efficiency.

Sloan and DuPont created a centralised budget for the corporation, instituted efficient control over the stock in-hand and co-ordinated retail demand with vehicle production. And, most importantly, Sloan set out to generate extra sales by encouraging people to trade in their cars when they went out of fashion, not when they had worn out. In short, Alfred P. Sloan created the annual model change policy, which hit at his principal rival, the Model T Ford, whose design was virtually immutable, and also countered the effect of second-hand deals on the new car market.

'I determined,' said Sloan, 'that my first job would be to concentrate all effort possible on making General Motors cars the very top in eye appeal, in engineering soundness, and in technological progress'.

Under Charles F. Kettering, the General Motors Research Laboratories kept the corporation ahead in the field of technological innovation, some of 'Boss Ket's' more spectacular developments being the reduction of engine knock by mixing tetraethyl lead with petrol and the first successful quick-drying paint finish for cars, conceived jointly with the DuPont chemical interests. This not only cut painting time from hours to minutes, but made it feasible to offer a wide choice of colour schemes, a facility of which maximum use was made by GM's styling wizard, Harley J. Earl. Kettering also developed an efficient two-stroke diesel—and this led to General Motors moving into the manufacture of railway engines and rolling stock, with the acquisition of the Winton Engine Company and the Electro-Motive Corporation in 1930.

Meanwhile, on the car front, Sloan had built up an enviably efficient dealer network. He spent a great deal of time travelling to dealers' meetings and to individual dealerships, sometimes visiting five in a day, creating a close working relationship between the Corporation and its dealers. Helping to cement the bond was the fact that GM offered a 24 per cent discount against Ford's 17 per cent.

By 1927, Sloan's reorganisation had resulted in a doubling of General Motors' profits, and the corporation had become one of the ten American companies valued at over $2,000,000,000; it was the only one of the ten that was set up along the lines of the most modern principles of industrial management. Chevrolet, especially, was riding high, with a total production of 700,000 in the first six months of 1927, equalling the output of the previous twelve months. Ford dealers were switching to the Chevrolet franchise, discouraged by the flagging sales of the utilitarian Model T Ford.

Moreover, General Motors was now an international organisation: there were manufacturing plants in Britain and Germany, where GM had taken over Vauxhall and Opel to produce cars suited to the particular requirements of those markets, while sales outlets were operating in 125 countries. Chevrolets were assembled from Canadian-built components in Britain and Copenhagen, while Buicks had been built in Britain since before World War I.

The corporation had moved into a new element in the late 1920s by acquiring a number of aviation companies. Of these, the most successful was Allison, an Indianapolis-based firm which began building aero engines in the 1930s, and became a major producer in this field during World War II. GM also acquired the Fokker Aircraft Corporation and a 24 per cent interest in the Bendix Aviation Corporation. Fokker, later the General Aviation Corporation, was absorbed by North American Aviation in 1933, though GM retained their interest in this company and Bendix until 1948.

Like all the other American car manufacturers, General Motors suffered severely from the 1929 Depression, but this time there was no repetition of the financial scares of the 1920 slump. Under Sloan's guidance, the corporation rode out the storm, and made a convincing recovery. When he retired as president in 1937, to become chairman of the board, GM was building 40 per cent of all the cars made in America, and 35 per cent of world production. Chevrolet was topping the domestic market, and the company also offered the Cadillac, La Salle, Buick, Oldsmobile and Pontiac marques, as well as GMC and Chevrolet trucks. It was the greatest industrial empire in history.

Sloan was succeeded by Knudsen, who headed General Motors through the war, in which they produced $12,000,000,000 worth of munitions, two-thirds of it made up of items they had never built before. The effort wore Knudsen out, and he died in 1948. The next president, Charles E. Wilson, known as 'Engine Charlie' to distinguish from 'Electric Charlie' Wilson, who headed General Electric, later became President Eisenhower's Secretary of Defence.

By the 1950s, General Motors could boast that it had 50 per cent of the American market; when the Senate checked out Engine Charlie's credentials for his post in the Eisenhower administration, he remarked with a straight face: 'What is good for the country is good for General Motors, and what is good for General Motors is good for the country'.

Indeed, the massive organisation that Sloan (who lived on well into his 90s) built, has far more money and resources at its disposal than many countries of the world—although the United States Department of Justice has had one or two things to say about monopolies in the past couple of decades. The corporation has diversified into several fields, including aero-engines, diesel locomotives, earthmovers, rockets, electronics, fridges, dishwashers, electric fires and ball-bearings.

Following Alfred Sloan's inspired marketing policy, however, their most important products are still 'cars for every purse and every purpose'.

PD

Above: the GM central technical studios at Warren, Michigan. The unusual steel dome is almost 4 inches thick. The building stands over sixty feet high and is one hundred and seventy feet wide

WORLD OF SPEED/**German Grand Prix**

THE 'CIRCUS' AT THE 'RING'

Right: John Surtees, Ferrari, pulls out a gaping lead over Jimmy Clark's Lotus in the 1963 race at the Nürburgring. At the end of the race, Surtees finisned over a minute ahead of Clark

THE GERMAN GRAND PRIX is traditionally associated with the famous Nürburgring, but it has also been run on two other tracks, Avus and Hockenheim.

In the early days of motor racing, the only Grand Prix race was the French GP but after World War I, other nations gradually began to hold Grand Prix races and in 1926, the first German Grand Prix was held. It took place at the Avus track near Berlin, an artificial race track having two parallel straights with a tight hairpin turn at one end and vast 43 degree banking at the other end. Rudolph Caracciola won the first Grand Prix in a supercharged 2-litre Mercedes at a speed of 84.5 mph but, even at those lowly speeds, there were three deaths, followed by complaints about the state of the track surface and for 1927, the race was switched to the newly completed Nürburgring.

Building of the Nürburgring had begun in 1925, mainly to give employment to the mass of unemployed men in the Eifel mountain district. The scheme was one of the most ambitious ever undertaken in the motor-racing world, for the 17.58 mile track had to be torn from a hilly and heavily forested area close to the small town of Adenau. The German government underwrote the cost of the track largely because they hoped it would also become a development track for the German motor industry. The track eventually became the most complete motor-racing facility in Europe with a hotel, garages for all the cars, a timing tower and concrete pits.

The first race at the 'Ring in 1927 attracted a crowd of 75,000 who had trekked from all parts of Germany. Not a patch on the 200,000 who regularly visited Avus, but the 'Ring was not as close to large population centres. The full 17 mile circuit was used for the first race, the winner being Otto Merz in a 6.8-litre Mercedes, who covered the 18 laps (316.5 miles) in just under 5 hours at a speed of 63.38 mph.

Even more spectators arrived for the 1928 Grand Prix which was again won by a Mercedes driven by Carraciola and Werner at the slightly higher speed of 64.5 mph. As before, the race was for sports cars and the first British entry, a $4\frac{1}{2}$-litre Bentley driven by Tim Birkin, finished eighth.

The Mercedes were beaten for the first time in 1929 when the massive 7-litre blown Mercedes had to give best to the fleet little 2-litre Bugatti of Louis Chiron who not only won but increased the overall speed to 66.42 mph and made a new fastest lap at 69.97 mph. There was no German Grand Prix in 1930 because of the severe depression which had hit the world, but it returned in 1931 to be run over 22 laps of the 14 mile north circuit. The track was so constructed that two different circuits could be used but, after 1929, the south circuit was seldom used. The race was run in torrential rain most of the time and Rudolph Caracciola in a specially-lightened sports 7-litre SSKL Mercedes showed his skill by running away from the field and winning at 67.29 mph. Chiron finished second in his Bugatti with Tazio Nuvolari third.

Mercedes temporarily withdrew from racing in 1932, so Carraciola moved to Alfa Romeo to drive their 2.6-litre single seaters. He led the works team to a 1, 2, 3 victory at the 'Ring, averaging 74.13 mph for the 354.35 mile race.

The Grand Prix was not held in 1933, the year Hitler came to power, but Hitler was quick to visualise the publicity value of motor-racing victories, and he offered tempting monetary rewards to German manufacturers who were successful in Grand Prix racing. Mercedes and Auto Union built cars for the 1934 season, beginning an era of domination which lasted until the outbreak of war in 1939. The grid for the 1934 German GP held three Mercedes and three Auto Unions, while a 200,000 strong crowd of patriotic Germans thronged the trackside enclosures. After a thrilling battle between Caracciola's Mercedes and Hans Stuck's vicious V16, rear-engined Auto Union, Stuck finally won when the Mercedes retired, leaving Fagioli's Mercedes to salvage second place.

The Germans were expected to run away with the 1935 race, but they reckoned without the 'Flying Mantuan', Tazio Nuvolari, driving an outclassed 3.2-litre Alfa Romeo, against the 4-litre Mercedes giving over 390 bhp. After a disastrously slow pit stop in mid race, Nuvolari dropped back to sixth place but, driving like a demon, he picked off car after car until he got to second place behind Brauchitsch's Mercedes.

German Grand Prix/WORLD OF SPEED

Top: the start of the 1963 German Grand Prix, and Graham Hill (BRM) peers anxiously to his right to check the whereabouts of arch-rival Jim Clark (Lotus-Climax). Both men, however, should have been watching their mirrors for the man putting a wheel over the white line on the left-hand side of the picture. This was eventual winner John Surtees and his Ferrari

He closed the gap on the big German car and on the last lap had to gain 27 seconds, and when he had closed to little more than 200 yards behind the Mercedes, it suddenly burst a tyre and Nuvolari swept by to win a dramatic victory. That year, the race had been reduced to 22 laps (311 miles) and Nuvolari won at 75.16 mph despite a wet circuit.

The year 1936 belonged to Auto Union and it was Bernd Rosemeyer who led them to victory at 81.8 mph with Hans Stuck second. Rosemeyer had lapped the 14 mile circuit in 9 minutes 56.6 seconds to average 85.5 mph for the fastest lap.

By 1937, the Auto Union V16, 6-litre engine gave no less than 520 bhp while the straight-eight Mercedes 5.6-litre unit gave a staggering 646 bhp. Against this sort of power, their rivals were in a hopeless position and Caracciola won from von Brauchitsch.

The Grand Prix formula for 1938 was reduced to 3 litres supercharged but Mercedes built a new V12 engine which gave 420 bhp, while Auto Union also had a new V12 which gave around 400 bhp. The Grand Prix was a triumph for Britain's Dick Seaman who had joined Mercedes the previous year; he was always well placed and, when team-mate von Brauchitsch's car caught fire at the pits he went on to a comfortable win from the Carraciola/Lang Mercedes.

In 1939, with World War II only a couple of months away, Mercedes again conquered the Nürburgring, this time Caracciola living up to his nickname of Regenmeister (rain master) by splashing through to win at a modest 75.31 mph from Muller's Auto Union.

At the end of the war, Germany was in no position to run any motor racing and, even if they were, the Nürburgring had been badly damaged by the passage of troops back and forth. However, by 1949, the track had been resurfaced and the FIA allowed the Germans to run the Grand Prix in 1950. They ran it for Formula Two cars, and victory went to Alberto Ascari's 2-litre Ferrari at 77.67 mph. The race had been shortened to 16 laps (226.7 miles).

Formula One racing returned in 1951 along with the mighty 1½-litre supercharged Alfa Romeos and 4½-litre Ferraris. Ascari's Ferrari beat the Alfa Romeo of Fangio over the 20 lap race at a speed of 83.71 mph.

For 1952, the race returned to Formula Two because Formula One had virtually died for lack of entries. Ascari, in a 2-litre Ferrari, completed his hat trick at the 'Ring from the similar cars of Farina and Fischer. The 2-litre racers returned in 1953, among them several new British cars like the Connaught, and Cooper while names like Stirling Moss, Roy Salvadori and Mike Hawthorn were early signs of the British invasion to come. Hawthorn was driving for the works Ferrari team and he finished third behind Farina's Ferrari and Fangio's Maserati.

The 2½-litre Formula One came in for 1954, and Mercedes returned to Formula One racing with a new straight-eight 270 bhp car. Naturally, a huge crowd, estimated at 350,000, flocked to the 'Ring to see the 'Silver Arrows' and they were not disappointed, for Fangio gave them victory at 82.77 mph from the Ferrari shared by Gonzalez and Hawthorn. In practice, Fangio had at last beaten Herrman Lang's 1939 lap record of 9 mins 52.2 secs with a lap in 9 mins 50.1 secs which shows how fast the big pre-war Mercedes had been.

The German GP was cancelled in 1955 because of the Le Mans tragedy, but it was back at the 'Ring again in 1956 where Fangio won again for Ferrari, setting a new lap record of 9 mins 41.6 secs (87.74 mph). The 1957 race was Fangio's greatest victory. He started the race in his 250F Maserati having only half a tank of fuel because he would need a stop for tyres anyway. He sliced into the lead and was well clear of Britain's Mike Hawthorn and Peter Collins in works Ferraris. However, his pit stop took over 50 seconds and the Ferraris were half a minute ahead of him when he rejoined the race. But he repeatedly slashed the lap record, finally leaving it at an unbelievable 9 mins 17.4 secs (91.53 mph) as he whipped past the British pair to win by just 3 seconds.

The first win by a British car in the German GP came in 1958 when Tony Brooks drove a Vanwall to victory from the Coopers of Salvadori and Trintignant. The race saw the death of Peter Collins who crashed while holding off Brooks for the lead. Brooks'

German Grand Prix

Above: practice for the 1973 German GP. Driven by Jackie Stewart and François Cevert, the Elf Team Tyrrells, pictured in the foreground, scored a convincing 1–2 victory

The year 1962 was Graham Hill's in the V8 BRM which he conducted through torrential rain to a popular victory from Surtees' Lola. Surtees had his revenge the next year when driving for Ferrari because he beat Jim Clark's Lotus by over a minute and set a new lap record of 8 mins 47.0 secs (96.81 mph). Surtees repeated the victory in 1964 in a V8 Ferrari with Graham Hill second in a BRM. He again lowered the record, this time to 8 mins 39.0 secs.

The first 100 mph lap came in practice for the 1965 race when Jim Clark lapped in 8 mins 22.7 secs (101.53 mph) with his V8 Lotus-Climax. The brilliant Scotsman made no mistake in the race either, beating Hill's BRM into second place once more, and setting a lap record of 8 mins 24.1 secs (101.22 mph).

The 3-litre Formula One arrived in 1966, and with it came the domination of the Brabham team. Jack Brabham won a very wet race at a modest 86.7 mph in his Brabham-Repco, and went on to take the World Championship very comfortably. It was Denny Hulme's turn to win for Brabham in 1967 with his boss, Jack Brabham, second; Hulme averaged 101.4 mph for the 15 laps with Dan Gurney putting in fastest lap at 8 mins 15.1 secs (103.1 mph).

A further reduction in distance to 14 laps (198 miles) came in 1968 and the circuit was running with water as Jackie Stewart tip-toed his Matra-Ford to victory at 86.8 mph from Graham Hill's Lotus 49. The 1969 race was Jacky Ickx's, the young Belgian flinging his Brabham-Ford round incredibly fast to beat Stewart's Matra and to put in the first sub-8 minute lap in 7 mins 43.8 secs (110.1 mph).

The 1970 season was a controversial one, for many drivers were upset by the deaths of comrades like Jim Clark, Bruce McLaren and Piers Courage and they began to demand more safety measures at circuits. The Nürburgring did not meet their requirements, so the race was switched to the artificial stadium circuit at Hockenheim, near Stuttgart which was, ironically, the circuit where Jim Clark lost his life. The circuit used was 4.22 miles long, having two long straights and a twisty 'Mickey Mouse' section in front of the stands. This fast circuit gave Jochen Rindt victory in his Lotus 72 at a speed of 123.9 mph over the 50 laps.

By 1971, the safety measures demanded by the drivers had been carried out at the 'Ring at an estimated cost of one million pounds. This produced a big jump in lap speeds and Jackie Stewart won in his Tyrrell-Ford at 114.4 mph from his team-mate, François Cevert, who put in fastest lap at 116.1 mph. The race had been further reduced in distance to 12 laps (170 miles) which took Stewart a modest 1½ hours to complete, against the near 5 hours of the early races.

The race distance was increased to 14 laps for 1972 to prevent the race going below the minimum time allowed for a Grand Prix and this time Jacky Ickx, driving a Ferrari 312, showed his class by winning at an average speed of 116.63 mph.

The 1973 race was a demonstration by Jackie Stewart of his mastery of the Nürburgring, for he led from start to finish in his Tyrrell, covering the 14 laps at 116.82 mph with his number two, Cevert, second.

The 1974 event proved to be a comfortable win for the ultra-powerful Ferrari of Clay Reggazoni, from a hard-driven Tyrrell-Ford of Jody Scheckter and a Brabham-Ford handled by Carlos Reutemann.

No greater demonstration of the enormous progress in racing-car design can be given than to compare the lap record of 1927 (15 mins 51.6 secs—66.59 mph) with Niki Lauda's unofficial practice time, in a Ferrari 312 B3, of 6 mins 58 secs. In 46 years, the lap time has been more than halved.

MT

team mate, Moss, made fastest lap in a new record of 9 mins 9.2 secs (92.90 mph).

The lack of German cars and drivers caused some poor gates at the 'Ring in 1957 and '58, so the organisers switched the race back to Avus for the second and last time in 1959. The race resulted in another victory for Tony Brooks, this time in a Ferrari, who won the two-heat race and put in a fastest lap at 149.14 mph—nearly twice as fast as that first German GP in 1926.

For 1960, the race went back to Nürburgring, but not to the main circuit. For the first time, the race was held on the short south circuit of 4.8 miles and, since the Germans had a competitive Formula Two car, the Porsche, the race was held for F2 cars. This paid off, for Sweden's Jo Bonnier won in a Porsche, covering the 32 lap race at 80.28 mph.

In 1961, it was back to the main north circuit and a reduction to 15 laps (211.8 miles) for the new 1½-litre Formula One. Driving Rob Walker's under-powered Lotus, Stirling Moss put on one of his greatest performances, beating the Ferraris of von Trips and Phil Hill comfortably.

Famous son of a famous father

Below: Peter Gethin, pictured right, driving the VDS Team Chevron B24 Formula 5000 machine, the car with which he won the 1973 Tasman series

MANY YOUNG MEN tend to be influenced by the chosen career of their fathers but Peter Gethin, born on 21 February 1940, the son of Ken Gethin, the famous flat-race jockey, ignored the turf and chose tarmac instead.

Like so many sons of famous fathers, his academic career was not notable, and he led a rather rootless life until he moved into motor racing. He soon found the excitement he was looking for, and in 1962, at the age of 22, he took up racing with a Lotus 7. He soon decided that single-seater racing was the only path to the top though, and he switched to a Formula Three Brabham. He took part in many races in Britain and Europe, joining the famous circus of drivers who toured the Continent, living from hand to mouth, often sleeping in their cars and spending all their money on their racing cars. This way of life continued for several years with no great success coming his way. He moved to a B7 Formula Three Chevron in 1967, and began to pick up a few good placings. By 1968, he had moved into Formula Two, racing both a Brabham and a Chevron, but there were many Grand Prix drivers taking part in Formula Two at that time and Gethin made only a modest impact against the tough opposition.

The breakthrough came when he decided to desert the established formulae and take a chance with the fledgling Formula 5000 for single-seaters powered by 5-litre stock-block engines. He was given the opportunity of driving the factory-supported McLaren M10A run by Church Farm Racing. These cars were as powerful as the current Formula-One machines, and Peter showed that he could handle the power and cope with the difficult handling of the big cars by winning three races in a row—the Guards F5000 race at Oulton Park, the Kent Messenger F5000 race at Brands Hatch and the Guards race at Mallory Park. He took his car to the USA for a spell of racing in their equivalent Formula A but returned to take a fourth place at Hockenheim and win the Guards F5000 Championship from ex-Formula One Lotus driver Trevor Taylor who had also turned to F5000.

His victories naturally brought him to the attention of the McLaren team, and it seemed they would eventually give him a chance of driving in Formula One, but his chance came much earlier than he anticipated, for Bruce McLaren was tragically killed in a testing accident at Goodwood and then Denny Hulme received badly burned hands during a testing accident at Indianapolis. He took over the works Formula One McLaren M14A at the Dutch Grand Prix where he crashed the car, but he began to get the hang of F1 racing and he finished tenth in the Austrian GP, ninth in the Italian, sixth in the Canadian and fourteenth in the USA event. His sixth place in Canada earned him his first World Championship point.

Gethin also raced for the McLaren Can-Am team midway through the season when Dan Gurney was forced to leave the team because of contractual difficulties. He showed that he was equally at home in the McLaren M8D by winning the Road America race and finishing second at Edmonton and Donnybrooke. This gave him third place in the Can-Am Championship.

In Formula 5000, Gethin was virtually unbeatable. If his car was going well, he would win. Out of twenty F5000 races, he won no less than eight and finished second in two others. His victories came at Zandvoort, Castle Combe, the Silverstone Martini race, Mallory Park, Zolder, Anderstorp and Brands Hatch (twice), while he took second places at Oulton Park and Mondello in Ireland. His McLaren M10B had been immaculately prepared and run by Sid Taylor on behalf of the factory.

McLaren retained Gethin in the Formula One team for 1971, firstly with an M14A then with the new M19 model. He had very little success, although neither did his team leader, Denny Hulme, but McLaren decided to drop Gethin from the team before the Austrian GP in August. He was immediately snapped up to drive a P160 BRM by the factory and, in only his second drive with the team, he won the Italian Grand Prix in a classic finish in which he led a screaming five car group of cars across the line by mere inches. He also won the Rothmans Victory race at Brands Hatch which was stopped due to the crash which killed Jo Siffert.

Earlier in the season, Gethin had taken second place in the two-heat International Trophy race driving an F5000 McLaren, and he also took in several Interserie races using an ex-Can-Am McLaren. Against modest opposition, he won at Zolder and finished second at Keimola and the Norisring.

For 1972, he was retained by BRM but had a miserable season, hardly ever finishing a race. His only Championship point was a sixth at Monza. In Formula Two, he drove a Chevron-BDA where he put up some fine performances, notching up a victory at Pau and taking fourth place at Salzburgring.

Gethin lost his place with the BRM team for 1973 and, as no other Formula One team wished to sign him, he returned to Formula 5000 with a Chevron B24. He notched up several wins with the Chevron, none more welcome than when he outpaced all the Formula One cars in the Race of Champions at Brands Hatch, beating his former team leader, Denny Hulme into second place.

The Belgian Team VDS recruited Gethin to join Teddy Pilette in an attack on the 1973/1974 Tasman series in Australia and New Zealand. They proved to be the most competitive team in the series; Gethin scored in every round to take the Championship comfortably.

Gethin once again raced an updated Chevron B24 in European F5000 races during 1974 with much success in the early-season races. MT

THE MOTOR INDUSTRY/Ghia

THE 'DIOR' OF MOTORING FASHION

Motoring fashions change almost as quickly as women's fashions. The task of the Ghia company is to reflect and anticipate the motoring public's concept of good taste

Whatever the Ghia design team turns its hand to, the results are a delight to study. An interesting observation too, is that the company is highly versatile and is equally at home producing attractive city cars (*bottom*) as it is producing one-off prototypes such as this De Tomaso 2+2 (*near right*) and high-speed small series production cars like the De Tomaso Mangusta (*far right*). Since the Ghia's inception in 1915, it has been responsible for many exciting motor cars. The company has now been bought by Ford of America

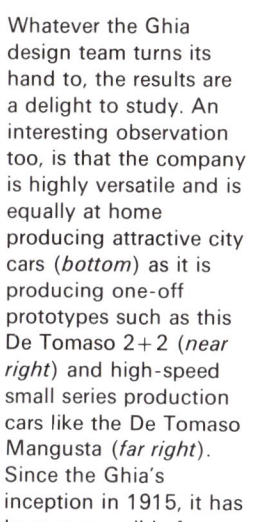

Ghia/THE MOTOR INDUSTRY

Left: the men responsible for much of the success enjoyed by the Ghia Company; Jack Head, President, confers with his chief stylists Tom Tjaarda (*left*) and Filipo Sapino

Below: first presented at the 1937 Milan Show, this is Ghia's Lancia Aprilia cabriolet

Bottom: another famous company to use the services of Ghia's design expertise was Delahaye. Together they produced the Delahaye 135M 3.5-litre of 1948

Opposite page, top right: stylists at work on a prototype

Centre: the Ghia-designed Alfa Romeo 2500SS of 1950

Bottom: in 1956, Ghia designed this four-seater tourer, called a Dart, for the Chrysler Corporation. It was powered by a 400 bhp Chrysler motor

THE HIGH FASHION CAPITAL FOR CLOTHES will always be Paris, however much London swings. Motoring's fashion city is Turin, and probably will be when cars are atomic powered and the wheel becomes a museum piece, for only in Turin does one find that unique feeling for the automobile as an art form. In scores of design studios and workshops, men create their dream cars in a blending of imagination, flair, craftsmanship and engineering skill which can turn a brainwave which might come to a designer, while sipping his aperitif, into a shining metal car body.

Because of the continuing love affair man has with his motor car, the Turin styling studios and specialist workshops still have a vital role to play in the automobile industry. Despite large-scale volume car production in places like Detroit, Coventry, Wolfsburg, Cologne and even Turin itself, dominating the industry, there is still a fundamental need for the forward-looking imagination and flair of the Italian stylists. They can design a model which will be produced in hundreds of thousands but with which the individual motorist can identify and reflect his personality, life-style and aspirations. So, while things are getting tough for the small-scale specialist car manufacturers in Turin and elsewhere, their creative talents are highly valued by the large companies in the industry.

Ghia Operations of Turin is typical of the styling houses. This famous design shop's skills have, for the past sixty years, been directed mainly towards an elite market. Nowadays, the Ghia stylists and craftsmen concentrate most of their efforts on products which most of us more ordinary mortals can afford. This

THE MOTOR INDUSTRY/Ghia

change of emphasis has happened since Ghia became part of the Ford organisation, and there are many other Turin 'motoring-fashion houses' with close relationships with such big manufacturers.

'The House of Ghia' began back in 1915 when Giacinto Ghia founded a small coachbuilding workshop in Turin, catering for an elite and exclusive clientele. Those first customers wanted big de luxe cars with daring lines, or refined sports cars. Then Ghia started associations with large manufacturers, and one of his first projects with the big boys was to create the 'Torpedo' high performance cars for Fiat who were also situated in Turin.

The Ghia plant was seriously damaged during World War II and Giacinto Ghia died, leadership of the firm passing to the young stylist Boano.

In 1950, Luigi Segre took over the management of Ghia and it was under him that the firm produced a series of special bodies for famous foreign chassis, including Delahaye, Bentley and Talbot. During the period of Segre's leadership, Ghia established connections with Detroit, and subsequently built prototypes or special models which included the Chrysler K 310, De Soto Coupé, Plymouth Explorer, Plymouth Adventurer, Plainsman, Norseman (which was lost when the liner Andrea Doria sank on its way to the United States) and the turbine-powered Turboflite.

Ghia's output of cars destined for production, like the Volkswagen 2+2 coupé, and exotic concept cars continued throughout the Fifties and Sixties. There was the famous Gilda of 1955 with its stabilising rear fins which represented a styling revolution, the Ferrari

Ghia/THE MOTOR INDUSTRY

Above, top to bottom: front and rear views of the Chrysler Dart of 1956;

the futuristic Gilda of 1955

Above right, top to bottom: a 1960 Chrysler prototype;

a 1962 Plymouth Valiant St Regis prototype;

a 1960 prototype, based on Chrysler mechanicals and known as the L64

Superamerica, Renault Floride, Volvo P 1800, the 'Jolly' cars on Fiat chassis and, for Ford, the Turnpike Cruiser, Bimini, and Futura.

It was a great loss to Ghia—and to motoring generally—when Luigi Segre died in 1963 at the age of 44. Gino Rovere took over as general manager, only to die the following year and be succeeded by Segre's former secretary, Giacomo Gaspardo Motor.

In 1967, An American company, Rowan Controller Co of Westminster, Maryland, bought Ghia and appointed Alessandro de Tomaso as President and Chairman of the Board. Ghia went on to produce the Ford-powered Mangusta and Pantera mid-engined sports cars, prototypes like the Vanessa woman's car, Pampero and Iso Fidia. Bodies were produced for the Maserati Ghibli and Spyder and for the Sno-Ghia tracked vehicle.

In 1970, the Ford Motor Company bought 80% of Ghia's shares from Rowan Controller, and Jack Head, one of Ford's most experienced finance executives, joined the company to assist Alessandro de Tomaso, who continued as President. This merger with Ford increased the pace of Ghia's operations, and the Pantera became one of the best selling mid-engined sports cars in the world. Work expanded also on the design and construction of prototypes for Ford.

De Tomaso resigned in December 1972 and Ford bought the remaining 20 per cent of Ghia shares held by him. Ghia Operations was founded, incorporating the Turin Design Centre of Ford Italiana, with Jack Head as Chief Executive. Ghia's role within Ford is that of a 'think tank' where ideas can be born, developed and then considered for volume production by the company's plants around the world. Also, Ghia's design and prototype work has increased and two new models made their début at the 1973 Geneva Show. The Ghia Mark I prototype was a luxury-car study based on the Ford Granada and the Mustela II, a theme car for future Ford production models. The first Ford production car to carry the Ghia name was the Mustang II, launched in September 1973, closely followed by Ghia versions of the Granada and Capri II in 1974.

Now perhaps more than ever before in its long history, Ghia is more closely involved in the harsh realities of mainstream motoring. However, the designers in this Turin studio are still able to exercise their creative flair in more free-ranging areas, as was demonstrated at the 1974 Geneva Show. Senior stylist Tom Tjaarda produced a styling study of how the Capri II might look towards the end of this century. His three-seater wedge-shaped car was the talk of the show, combining aerospace technology with advanced

THE MOTOR INDUSTRY/Ghia

Right: borrowing a famous name from the past, this is the 1970 6.6-litre Pontiac-engined Stutz Duplex, designed by Virgil Exner

Below centre: based on Plymouth Barracuda mechanicals, the Ghia 450SS

Bottom: Ghia's Ford Cobra, based on the 7-litre version of the Carroll Shelby-inspired AC Cobra

Below right: shown at the 1969 Turin Show, Ghia's Lancia 1600 prototype

Ghia/THE MOTOR INDUSTRY

auto safety features. Controversy raged around the car at the show and, subsequently, in the world's motoring press. Once again, Ghia demonstrated its flair and ability to be daring and unconventional.

The Ghia styling house comprises a team of eight designers producing the ideas and detailed specifications which skilled Italian craftsmen turn into clay, plaster and plastic-foam models. If these look promising, then the Ghia metal beaters turn them into prototype vehicles—often at incredible speed.

Ghia can work very quickly when the pressure is on, as was shown with 'Project Ancona', a prototype which greatly influenced the final design of Mustang II. In only 53 days, a paper drawing was transformed into a driveable car with a quality of finish that is the hallmark of all Ghia products. Ford's President, Lee Iacocca, was delighted. He had asked Ghia for ideas, and, in just under two months, they had produced a car he could sit in, drive and really assess as a replacement for the Mustang I.

Ghia has come a long way since Giacinto set up his small workshop in Turin sixty years ago. There have been many changes in motoring fashions as well as women's clothes since then, with Ghia of Turin, like Dior of Paris, helping to lead the way by both reflecting and anticipating the influences on society's concepts of good taste; a task which Ghia have accepted and responded to superbly. CH

Top: the Thor 2+2, based on the Oldsmobile Toronado, is yet another of the company's designs

Centre: the superb Ghia-styled De Tomaso Pantera. This car caused such a stir in the motoring world that the Ford Motor Company decided to take a closer look at the Ghia organisation, eventually buying it out

Bottom: one of the first results of the collaboration between Ghia and Ford was the Ford Granada Ghia coupé, a more refined version of the standard saloon model

THE GREAT CARS/Gilbern

THE INVADERS FROM WALES

The Gilbern company was founded in 1959, and, until its closure in 1974, produced the only complete car to be manufactured in Wales

UNTIL THEIR DEMISE early in 1974, Gilbern had the distinction of being the only motor manufacturers making complete cars in Wales.

The company came into being when a German ex-prisoner of war, Bernard Frieze, began working for a company which specialised in the use of glassfibre. He decided to build himself a car using glassfibre bodywork and, when this special was finished, it caught the attention of Giles Smith, who ran a butchery business in Llantwit Fardre near Pontypridd, Glamorgan. The two men joined together to build a modified version of the original car in a workshop behind the butcher's shop and in 1959 they decided to go into production with the car, setting up in a small factory in Llantwit Fardre. It was decided to call the new car Gilbern simply by using the first parts of the two men's Christian names.

The first car, the Gilbern GT Mk 1, was a two-plus-two, two-door coupé largely using BMC components. The car featured a steel-tube chassis with large diameter side members and built up sections at the front to take the BMC double-wishbone front suspension, and at the rear to hold the mountings for the BMC live rear axle which was mounted on coil-spring/damper units and located by radius arms. Braking was by 9 inch front discs and 8 inch rear drums, steering being by BMC rack-and-pinion. Originally, three choices of engine were offered to customers; a BMC A series 948 cc unit fitted with a Shorrocks supercharger, a Coventry Climax 1098 cc single-overhead-camshaft racing engine and the 1558 cc BMC engine as fitted to the MGA. The supercharged engine proved rather temperamental and the Coventry Climax engine never caught on, so the only unit sold in any numbers was the MGA unit which gave the car a top speed of 100 mph and very brisk acceleration by the standards of the day. The glassfibre body was rather ugly and not very well finished on early examples, but improvements to the moulds were made and in their first year, eleven cars were built. The cars were usually sold as kits of parts but Gilbern trimmed the body completely so that owners merely had to bolt on the suspension and drop in the engine/gearbox unit. In kit form, the Mk 1 sold for £978.

By 1962, the 1622 cc MGA engine had been substituted for the smaller unit and production was running at a comfortable one car a week. Various improvements had been made, a small dealer network set up, and the car was beginning to become well known in specialist motoring circles.

The 1622 cc version carried on to the end of 1963 but this was then superseded by the 1798 cc MGB-engined car, and the model was renamed the Gilbern 1800 GT. Various improvements were made to the car including the addition of a Panhard rod for improved location of the rear axle and the option of Laycock de-Normanville overdrive as used on the MGB. The top speed had now risen to 110 mph.

The Gilbern was carving itself an increasing share of the GT market, its combination of four seats and good acceleration allied to a modest price more than making up for the rather dated styling. By 1965, production was up to three cars a week, still mostly sold in kit form.

In 1966, it was decided to build a completely new model, the Genie, which featured a new body and mechanical components taken from Ford and BMC models. The car still retained a square-tube space-frame-type chassis with double wishbone and coil-spring front suspension combined with an MGB live rear axle located by radius arms and a Panhard rod suspended on coil springs and telescopic dampers. The engine chosen for the new model was the Ford Zodiac V6 unit; with a capacity of 2994 cc, this engine produced a useful 144 bhp at 4750 rpm. The engine was mated to the four-speed Ford gearbox. The steering was once again the MGB rack-and-pinion unit and braking was by MGB 10¾ inch discs on the front wheels in conjunction with 10 inch rear drums. To overcome some of the inherent weaknesses of glassfibre bodywork, the doors were hung directly on the

Top: a 1971 Invader. Although looking very much like the earlier Genie, this car's revised suspension made the handling far superior to that of its predecessor

Above: not quite what it seems—this car is actually a 1968 Genie which was converted to estate-car form by its owner. This model bears a striking resemblance to the Invader estate of which 68 were built

Gilbern/THE GREAT CARS

Above: a 1973 Mk III Invader, one of the last cars to be produced by the company. Considering that the body design, in 1974, was almost eight years old, the car looks relatively undated. *Inset* is the car's sumptuous interior, complete with walnut dashboard, electric windows and an air of luxury

chassis frame so that they would not drop in service.

The glassfibre body was a great improvement on its predecessor, the new shape being a stylish slab-sided two-door coupé. Single headlamps were recessed into the wings and a full width grille was fitted. The main problem with the body was the large flat areas along the sides, for the makers found it impossible to eliminate the slight ripples in the surface finish. This problem stayed with the car to the end. The only other major problem with the car was in the steering geometry which tended to allow the steering wheel to go 'over centre' when cornering hard. This disconcerting tendency was gradually eliminated by changes to the suspension.

The top speed of the Genie was a healthy 120 mph with a 0–60 mph acceleration time of around 9 seconds. Since the rear seats offered more leg room than those of its predecessor, the car found a steady if not booming demand, and again most cars were sold in kit form at around £1500, although a completely built up car could be had for slightly under £2000.

Sales were not as promising as those of the old Mk 1 model, partly as a result of its price increase and partly because of increased competition. An injection of capital would obviously assist in financing further expansion so, in April 1968, the company was acquired by Ace Holdings Ltd of Cardiff, who themselves were shortly taken over by Mecca, the dance-hall and leisure group. Bernard Frieze and Giles Smith remained as directors, charged with the task of increasing the dealer network and boosting production from a modest two cars a week to five or more.

In late 1968, an additional version of the Genie was announced; this was basically the standard model fitted with Tecalemit Jackson fuel injection which boosted the power output to 165 bhp. The car was named the PI 130 (for petrol injection and the claimed top speed) but it found few takers.

The Genie continued in production until 1970 when it was replaced by the Invader, which was essentially the same car. The bodywork was virtually unchanged apart from improved door handles, but light-alloy wheels were now available, automatic transmission became an optional extra, the interior trim was improved and the front disc brakes were increased in diameter to 11.25 inches.

For 1971, an estate-car version of the Invader was announced. This was very similar to the saloon model in specification except that the roof line was carried further rearwards, and an opening tailgate fitted. The price of the estate was £1855 in kit form or £2384 ready assembled compared with £1745 for the saloon in kit form and £2247 built up.

Sales began a gradual decline in 1972 largely because mass-produced cars like the Ford Capri and MGB GT could be obtained much cheaper. Further problems were presented to the company with the introduction of VAT in April 1973, which virtually killed kit-car manufacture. Gilbern anticipated the ending of kit-car making and stopped building kits late in 1972, but the price of the saloon escalated dramatically to £2668 including VAT and the special car tax. This was almost as much as cars like the Jaguar XJ6 so demand for the Gilbern slumped considerably.

Another costly problem for Gilbern was the new safety and pollution laws which required them to crash test a car and satisfy exhaust pollution tests. Gilbern were able to gain a temporary exemption but sales would not support this costly undertaking and production ground to a halt in mid 1973. A Welsh property developer and financier read about Gilbern's troubles and negotiated a takeover bid. He quickly put the car back into production but the price had now risen to £2955, or £3098 with automatic transmission. This in itself was enough to sound the death knell of Gilbern but it was the Arab/Israeli war and the subsequent rise in petrol prices and drop in car sales that finally ended the life of Wales' only car maker. MT

THE GREAT CARS/Ginetta

CAR BUILDING— A FAMILY AFFAIR

The Ginetta company was created by the four Walklett brothers and after a varied career it is now recognised as one of Britain's most successful sports-car builders

THE GINETTA COMPANY was formed by four brothers, Bob, Douglas, Ivor and Trevor Walklett. Originally, they ran a general-engineering business at Woodbridge in Suffolk, but their enthusiasm lay with sports cars and, in the early 1950s, Ivor Walklett modified an old Wolseley Hornet which ran well until he crashed it in his own driveway. This machine, which later became known as the Ginetta G1, kindled the brothers' enthusiasm, and they decided to build a car for sale to the public. This car, the G2, was very similar to a Lotus 6, using a multi-tubular space frame and mechanical components from the Ford Popular. Quite a few kits were sold to enthusiasts who used their own mechanical components to complete the cars.

The G2 was handicapped to some extent by its appearance, for it had a simple aluminium body which merely clothed the space frame, with cycle-type wings on all four wheels. The age of the Ford special was in full swing in the late 1950s, and many enthusiasts were fitting handsome-looking but frail glassfibre bodies to Ford Popular chassis. The Walkletts decided to build a car with a glassfibre body, the G3 being the result. This used a multi-tubular chassis which was again designed to take Ford components. The glassfibre body was of the all-enveloping type with such refinements as flush fitting headlights, a coupé body and even doors—items which the G2 could not boast!

This model sold quite well in kit form but Ivor Walklett, who carried out all the design work, had designed a successor, the G4, which appeared at the 1961 Racing Car Show. This car again featured a tubular-steel space frame, cut down at the sides to allow doors to be fitted. Front suspension was by double wishbones and coil spring/damper units from the Triumph Herald, while the Ford Anglia live rear axle was located by trailing arms and an 'A' bracket and suspended on coil spring/damper units. The G4 was clothed in a neat and pretty sports two-seater body, the flowing lines of which proved very popular with enthusiasts. It was made up in several pieces, the scuttle section being bonded to the 1 inch square 18 gauge chassis tubes, the bonnet and boot section being quickly detachable. A hood and sidescreens were provided and, although trim was spartan, the car appealed to enthusiasts, for it was sold at the low price of £499, which included all the components necessary to complete the car. The standard engine was the Ford Anglia 105E, but the 1340 cc Ford Classic engine was available for only an extra £16.

By 1962, Ginetta had moved to a new factory at Witham in Essex and were kept busy turning out the G4 for several years. In 1963, a G5 variant was introduced with the Ford Cortina 1498 cc engine. However, it was still known as the G4 by customers and soon the G5 tag was forgotten. A hardtop was offered with the G4 and G5 and, later, the hardtop was incorporated

Below: the Ginetta G21 was announced at the 1972 London Motor Show, but was not put into production until late in 1973. The car is available with a choice of 1725 cc Chrysler Rapier, 1725 cc Holbay Rapier H120 or 2994 cc Ford V6 engines. The attractive front-engined coupé has a steel chassis and glassfibre bodywork.

Ginetta/THE GREAT CARS

into the body to turn it into a coupé. Private owners began entering races with the G4, and the factory entered Chris Meek in a disc-braked version with independent rear suspension (the G4R)—an option available to customers incidentally. This tiny car, powered by a 1600cc pushrod Ford engine, created havoc among the bigger GT cars, invariably humbling Jaguar E-types and AC Cobras in club races. This helped push sales of the road cars among enthusiasts and, by the time production ended in 1967, over 500 G4s had been produced.

The company realised that, if they were to expand into the general motoring market, they had to get away from the G4 concept which was too spartan for the average driver, so they began development of the G10, a big two-door sports car powered by an American Ford V8 4.7-litre engine coupled to a four-speed gearbox. All-round independent suspension was fitted, with disc brakes on all wheels. The prototype was immediately entered in a race and Chris Meek beat all the E-types and the like with a completely undeveloped

Above: the smart Ginetta G15 coupé. This tiny rear-engined machine first appeared in 1967. It was fitted with the Hillman Imp Sport engine. Disc brakes were fitted at the front while drums were utilised at the rear

Right: at the same time as the G15 was announced, Ginetta produced the G16, a mid-engined sports/racing car. It was available with the V8 BRM 2-litre engine or the four-cylinder BRM or Coventry-Climax motors. The car, however, was not very successful and was dropped after a couple of seasons

THE GREAT CARS/Ginetta

car. The car was too expensive to build for the British market, and it was dropped after no more than six had been built. A cheapened version using an MGB engine, gearbox and rear axle was introduced, but the G11, as it was called, fared little better than the G10, because of the difficulty in obtaining components, only a dozen being built.

The G6 of 1963 had been a modified version of the G4 to take a three-cylinder, two-stroke DKW engine tuned by Dieter Mantzel. Mantzel took five or six of these to Germany and raced them with some success. The G7 was a prototype which was basically similar to the G4 but used a transaxle at the rear instead of a separate gearbox and rear axle. The G8 was an unusual all-glassfibre monocoque single-seater for F3 racing and Chris Meek took one to a third place on its first outing. However, the monocoque lacked sufficient torsional rigidity and was difficult to repair, so the model never progressed beyond the prototype stage. The G9 was a project for a space-frame Formula Two car which never got into the metal.

The competition car which took over from the G4 in 1966 was the G12, a mid-engined coupé with all-independent suspension, and discs all round. The early version was fitted with the Cosworth SCA 1000 cc engine and, in the hands of Willie Green and John Burton, the G12 trounced the opposition. Later versions with the Lotus–Ford twin-cam engine were not as successful, but over 50 were built, and a number were converted by owners for road use.

The designation G13 was not used for superstitious reasons, and the G14 was a backbone chassis prototype sports car, similar in concept to the Lotus Elan, but Ginetta felt that the backbone was not stiff enough for their standards and it was abandoned.

The next major road-car project was the G15, which appeared at the London Motor Show in 1967, but it did not go into production until August 1968. The G15 was a rear-engined two-door coupé of tiny proportions fitted with the Hillman Imp Sport engine and transaxle at the rear, complete with the trailing-arm rear suspension. This was all mounted on a steel

Below: one of the three engine options available on the Ginetta G21 is the Holbay-modified Chrysler Rapier H120 motor. The four-cylinder 1725 cc unit produces 95 bhp at 5000 rpm and enables the car to reach a top speed of 112 mph

Ginetta/THE GREAT CARS

chassis, the engine being underslung beneath the upswept chassis side members. Front suspension was by double wishbones and coil springs taken from the Triumph Spitfire. Disc brakes were fitted to the front wheels while drums were utilised at the rear. With 55 bhp available from the Imp Sport engine, the car was capable of 100 mph yet, because it weighed only 10 cwt, it could comfortably achieve 45 mpg. Initially, the car was sold at £849 in kit form but prices rose dramatically as the prices of bought-out materials, especially glassfibre, rose and by 1974 the price of a completely built-up car inclusive of VAT had risen to £1395. With further cost increases imminent in late 1974, Ginetta decided to cease production of the G15 in April after some 800 had been built. A G15S model was produced in small quantities, this model having a very full list of standard equipment together with the 1000 cc version of the Imp engine built by the Chrysler Competition department. Several successful racing versions were also built, notably the works-backed car of Barry Wood.

At the same time as the G15 was announced, Ginetta also built another mid-engined sports/racing car. This followed the pattern of the G12 but was available with the larger 2-litre BRM V8, four-cylinder BRM and Coventry Climax engines. The car was not as successful as the G12 and was eventually dropped after a couple of disappointing seasons.

Ginetta moved back into single-seater racing with the G17, 18 and 19. The G17 was a space-frame Formula Four car with Imp engine which proved to be quite successful; one example was driven by Peter Voight in hill-climbs with considerable success. The G18 was a Formula Ford model which achieved some success, but Ginetta did not run a works car, so development was left to private owners. The G19 was a Formula Three version which never went into serious production because Ginetta had decided by this time to concentrate entirely on production of their successful road cars.

After a projected mid-engined road car, the G20, which never left the drawing board, the next production car was the G21. This was a fairly conventional front-engined two-door coupé, with steel chassis and glassfibre bodywork and a choice of Sunbeam Rapier, Rapier Holbay or Ford 3-litre engines. Suspension was by double wishbones at the front combined with a live axle on coil springs at the rear. The Ford 3-litre version was also available with independent rear suspension as a special option.

Production of the G21 commenced in 1973 after it and the G15 had satisfactorily completed the crash tests at the Motor Industry Research Association track at Nuneaton. The G21 was the sole production Ginetta in 1974, as the company was diversifying into several other fields.   MT

Above: the Ginetta G15 in action. Production was ended in April 1974 after some 800 of the sleek little coupés were built. The G15 was replaced by the more powerful and spacious front-engined G21 model

CARS OF TODAY/Ginetta

GINETTA G21

The Ginetta company has built many varied cars over its relatively short history. Their models have ranged from specialist racing cars to a pretty little Hillman Imp-based road car, the G15. It would be quite fair to say that the G15 really put the Ginetta company on the map as far as the sporting motorist was concerned, and when the company decided to drop the Imp-powered car and produce a more powerful and larger replacement the firm could be certain that their new car would attract quite a lot of attention.

The new car, the G21, was announced at the 1972 London Motor Show but was not put into production until late in 1973. It has a choice of three engines: the famous Ford Essex 3-litre V6, the Chrysler 1725 cc Rapier engine and the Holbay-tuned Rapier H120 engine. Either the Ford or Chrysler gearboxes are used for the respective engines, with Laycock-de Normanville overdrive being optional on the Chrysler-engined models.

The suspension at the front is by wishbones, coil springs, an anti-roll bar and telescopic dampers, while the rear is by a rigid axle, longitudinal trailing arms and a transverse linkage bar (Chrysler-engined versions) or by wishbones, semi-axles acting as upper arms, twin longitudinal radius arms, coil springs and telescopic dampers (Ford-powered version). Steering on all three models is by rack and pinion, while the stopping is taken care of by discs at the front and drums at the rear (Chrysler) or discs all round (Ford).

The top speed of the Ford-powered car is 127 mph and it accelerates to 60 mph in 7.8 secs, the Rapier-powered car can reach 112 mph and accelerates to 60 mph in 9.7 secs, while the H120 version has a top speed of 121 mph and accelerates to 60 mph in 8.5 secs. Fuel consumption ranges from 24 mpg (Ford) to 30 mpg (Rapier).

ENGINE Front-mounted water-cooled straight four or V6. 81.5 mm (3.21 in) bore × 82.5 mm (3.25 in) stroke = 1725 cc (105.3 cu in) (Chrysler-powered cars) or 93.7 mm (3.69 in) bore × 72.4 mm (2.85 in) stroke = 2994 cc (182.7 cu in) (Ford-powered cars). Maximum power 79 bhp at 5200 rpm (Rapier), 95 bhp at 5000 rpm (Rapier H120) or 140 bhp at 5300 rpm (Ford); maximum torque 91 lb ft at 3800 rpm (Rapier), 109 lb ft at 4300 rpm (Rapier H120) or 174 lb ft at 3000 rpm (Ford). Cast-iron cylinder block and cast-iron heads (Ford) or light-alloy head (Rapiers); compression ratio 9.2:1 (Rapier), 9.6:1 (Rapier H120) or 8.9:1 (Ford); 4 main bearings (Ford) or 5 main bearings (Rapier); 2 valves per cylinder operated by a single camshaft at centre of V (Ford), or at the side (Rapier). 1 Weber downdraught twin-barrel carburettor (Ford), 2 Zenith-Stromberg semi-downdraught carburettors (Rapier), or 2 Weber 40 DCOE carburettors (Rapier H120).

TRANSMISSION Single-dry-plate clutch and 4-speed manual gearbox. Ratios (Ford) 1st 3.163, 2nd 2.214, 3rd 1.412, 4th 1, reverse 3.346:1. Hypoid-bevel final drive with limited-slip differential, ratio 2.880. Ratios (Chrysler) 1st 3.122, 2nd 1.992, 3rd 1.295, 4th 1, reverse 3.322:1. Hypoid-bevel final drive, ratio 3.700.

CHASSIS Tubular frame.

SUSPENSION Front—independent by means of wishbones, coil springs, an anti-roll bar and telescopic dampers; rear—non independent by a rigid axle, longitudinal trailing arms and a transverse linkage bar (Chrysler) or independent by wishbones, semi-axles acting as upper arms, twin trailing longitudinal radius arms, coil springs and telescopic dampers (Ford).

STEERING Rack and pinion.

BRAKES Disc front and rear (Ford), or disc front, drums rear (Chrysler).

WHEELS 5½ in light alloy.

TYRES 165 × 13.

DIMENSIONS AND WEIGHT Wheelbase 91 in; track—front 50.75 in—rear 51 in (Ford) or 50.50 in (Chrysler); length 156.50 in; width 63 in; height 46 in; ground clearance 4.75 in; kerb weight 1920 lb (Ford) or 1890 lb (Chrysler); turning circle 35 ft; fuel tank capacity 10 gals.

BODY 2-door, 2-seat coupé.

PERFORMANCE Maximum speed 127 mph (Ford), 112 mph (Rapier) or 121 mph (Rapier H120). Acceleration 0–60 mph 7.8 secs (Ford), 9.7 secs (Rapier) or 8.5 secs (Rapier H120). Fuel consumption between 24 and 30 mpg over whole range.

One of America's best

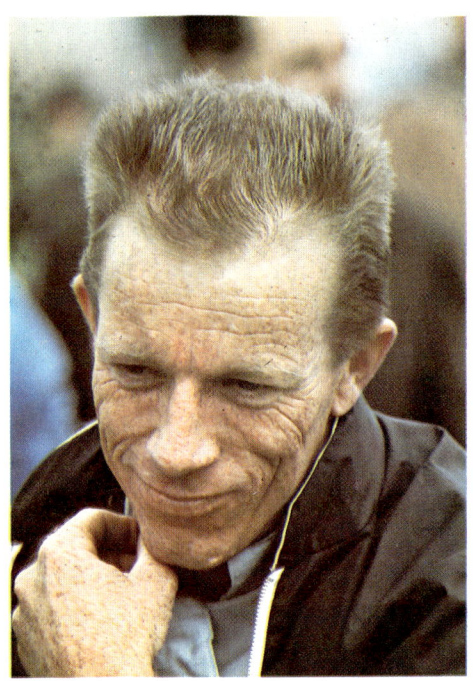

Above: Richie Ginther in action in the 1.5-litre Honda V12, during the 1965 Belgian Grand Prix at Spa. Later that year Ginther won the Mexican Grand Prix

FOR A LONG SPELL IN THE LATE 1950s and early 1960s, America's Richie Ginther was one of the world's leading Grand Prix drivers, offering formidable opposition to the European aces, along with his countrymen Phil Hill and Dan Gurney, who showed that the 'colonies' could provide racing drivers of the highest calibre.

Born in Los Angeles in 1930, Paul Richard Ginther was given a grounding in motor engineering and began work as a motor mechanic. He moved to Santa Monica where his interest in motor racing led him into a friendship with Phil Hill who, in 1950, was just beginning his international career. With Hill's encouragement, Ginther took up racing himself with an MG TC, but two years National Service as an aircraft mechanic kept him off the tracks until 1953. In that year, Hill invited Ginther to ride with him as mechanic in his Ferrari on the famous Mexican Road Race. They crashed, but Ginther's enthusiasm was not dampened and he returned for a further spell in the passenger's seat the following year when Hill drove a 4½-litre Ferrari into second place.

Ginther returned to his work as a car mechanic when he left the services but he chose to work for dealers who ran racing teams and, before long, he was being invited to race the machines he prepared. He handled sports cars like the vicious 4.9-litre Ferrari and an Aston Martin DB3S, but it was with a Porsche Spyder that Ginther's name really came to public notice, for he won several races in Sports Car Club of America events.

Phil Hill was firmly entrenched as a works Ferrari driver in the late 1950s and it was no doubt his persuasion that caused Enzo Ferrari to invite Ginther to Europe. He had, in fact, already made a trip to Europe to drive a 2-litre Ferrari for Luigi Chinetti in the 1957 Le Mans race without making any great impact, but Ferrari was well disposed towards American drivers since he felt that this encouraged sales of his road cars in the USA.

Ginther joined the Ferrari team in 1960 and, despite having famous team mates like Phil Hill, Wolfgang von Trips, Willy Mairesse and Cliff Allison, he showed that he was a first class driver. He finished second in the Buenos Aires 1000 km race with von Trips, then took sixth place in the Monaco GP on his Grand Prix *début* and followed up with second place in the Italian GP at the Monza circuit.

Ferrari soon appreciated Ginther's engineering talent and he was given the task of track testing all new Ferrari models as well as being a team member of both the sports-car and Grand Prix teams. With the new 1½-litre Ferrari in 1961, Ginther usually had to give best to his more experienced team mates but he finished a memorable second at Monaco when Stirling Moss' underpowered Lotus outwitted the Ferraris; only Ginther could get within striking distance of the maestro. He also took third place in the Belgian and British GPs and a fifth in the Dutch GP to end up with fifth place in the World Championship. In sports-car racing, he co-drove with von Trips to second place in the Sebring 12 Hours and third at the Nürburgring.

Ferrari did not pay their drivers very well in the early 1960s, so Ginther defected to BRM in 1962 where he again had to play second fiddle, this time to Graham Hill who won the World Championship. However, Ginther finished second in the Italian GP, third in the French GP and third in the Natal GP in South Africa with the 1½-litre V8 BRM. He remained with BRM in 1963, taking second place at Monaco and Monza and third in the French GP, to tie with team leader Hill for second place in the Championship. He also finished second in the non-Championship Oulton Park Gold Cup.

For his final season with BRM, Ginther finished every World Championship race he started, although once again the elusive victory did not come his way. He finished second at Monaco again, eleventh in the Dutch GP, fourth in the Belgian, fifth in the French, eighth in the British, seventh in the German, second in the Austrian, fourth in the Italian, fourth in the US and eighth in the Mexican.

For the 1965 season, Ginther was invited to join the Honda team, but the 1½-litre V12 Japanese car was a troublesome machine and he usually finished well down the field. But in the final race of the 1965 season, the Mexican Grand Prix, the Honda held together and Ginther recorded his first and only GP victory.

Ginther had also raced for Ford in long-distance races but his only good finish was a third place in the 1965 Daytona 24 Hour race.

Ginther stayed with Honda in 1966 for the first season of the new 3-litre Formula but as the V12 car was not ready he drove a Cooper-Maserati occasionally, taking fifth place in the Belgian Grand Prix. Ginther crashed the Honda during its *début* at the Italian GP but he finished fourth in the Mexican GP.

For 1967, his countryman Dan Gurney asked Ginther to join him in running the Eagle-Weslake Formula One cars but they were very troublesome and, although Ginther practised several times, he never got into a race, and midway through the season he decided to retire.

The tiny, crew cut, carrot-haired Ginther was a much admired member of the Grand Prix circus, who was on the fringe of greatness. Since his retirement, he has concentrated on acting as team manager for various teams, notably the American Porsche importers' team. MT

THE GREAT CARS/**Glas**

FROM GOGGOMOBILS TO GRAND TOURERS

Hans Glas took a brave gamble when he launched the tiny Goggomobil onto the market. It proved so popular, however, that the company was soon rapidly expanding

Above: by 1965, the Glas company was offering a bewildering variety of machines for sale. One of these was this Glas 1300GT, fitted with a 1289 cc engine and featuring bodywork by the famed Frua company. Later, a 1700 cc engine, producing 100 bhp, was fitted and the car was marketed as the 1700GT

IN 1951, THE OLD-ESTABLISHED agricultural machinery firm of Hans Glas GmbH of Dingolfing, Germany, decided to move into the motoring field, firstly with a scooter and then with a proper car. The post-war crisis in Germany led to a boom in mini-cars and three-wheelers, with such machines as the Heinkel, Isetta and Messerschmitt gaining a good share of the market, especially in Britain where three-wheelers offered special advantages in low taxation and their availability to the holders of motor-cycle licences who wanted more comfort than two wheels could afford.

Glas decided to ignore the three-wheeler market and go for a really small car, the Goggomobil, which first appeared in 1955. This tiny two-door saloon was only 9 feet 6 inches long and featured swing-axle suspension front and rear, little 10 inch wheels, rack-and-pinion steering and drum brakes on all wheels. The engine was mounted at the rear of the car, the first unit offered being a twin-cylinder, two-stroke engine mounted transversely in the car. This was basically a motor-cycle engine which gave 13.6 bhp at 5400 rpm from its 247 cc, endowing the 8 cwt car with a top speed of 49 mph and a fuel consumption of more than 50 mpg. The four-speed transmission was a motor-cycle non-synchromesh gearbox in unit with a multi-plate wet clutch, an unusual feature being that the floor-mounted gear lever had to be operated by moving it across the car from side to side.

The Glas T250, as it was called, soon became popular with drivers who required a very basic economy car. Later, the engine was made available as a 296 cc unit, which gave 15 bhp at 5000 rpm and raised the top speed to 52 mph, while an even bigger version with a 395 cc capacity gave 18.5 bhp at 5000 rpm. This model, the T400, eventually became the most popular as it was capable of exceeding 60 mph yet still gave a very respectable fuel consumption of around 50 mpg.

Glas soon realised the possibilities of their little car and decided to bring out a coupé version. This pretty little machine with a body reminiscent of the Alfa Romeo Giulietta coupé was a great success with enthusiasts and, although it was available with the 250, 300 and 400 cc engines, it was seldom bought in anything but the 400 cc form. Mechanically, it was virtually the same as the saloon model but its superior aerodynamic shape gave it a top speed of around 65 mph. A delightful optional extra on the coupé was the French Cotal electric gearbox which gave fingertip gearchanging.

Several examples of the T400 coupé were raced with a moderate amount of success, notching up several class wins, mainly because of the negligible opposition.

With increasing prosperity, the demand for bigger cars grew, so in 1958 Glas introduced the new Isar T600 and T700 saloon, followed by an estate-car version. These models were quite conventional front-engined cars with rather ugly two-door bodies. Front

Glas/THE GREAT CARS

suspension was by an unusual combination of trailing upper wishbones and transverse lower arms in conjunction with coil springs and telescopic dampers, while the live rear axle was mounted on semi-elliptic leaf springs. Steering was cam-and-peg, drum brakes being fitted on all four wheels. Power came from a flat-twin, four-stroke engine which gave 19 bhp at 4800 rpm in 548 cc form and 30 bhp at 4900 rpm in 688 cc form. Although the T700 was capable of 70 mph, against the 60 mph of the T600, neither model really caught on and, even though they were still catalogued in 1964, production had slowed down to a mere dribble.

In 1961, Glas showed that they had ambitions of invading the car market in a big way by introducing a range of technically advanced cars. The Italian stylist Pietro Frua had been engaged to carry out body design, and he produced a handsome range of saloons, coupés and convertibles. The first models to emerge were the S1004 coupé and convertible, which had a chassis layout similar to that of the Isar except that the wheelbase was lengthened by 5 inches. The most interesting part of the car was the engine, an entirely new, four-cylinder, water-cooled single-overhead-camshaft unit. The camshaft operated inclined valves in a hemispherical combustion chamber and the camshaft was driven by an internally toothed cogged belt. This was one of the first applications of the exposed cogged-belt drive, and Glas found that it worked satisfactorily. With a cast-iron block, light alloy head and five main bearings, the engine proved to be a rugged unit, giving 42 bhp at 5000 rpm from its 992 cc. A four-speed, all-synchromesh gearbox was fitted and top speed for the coupé was about 85 mph. Mechanically, the convertible was identical to the coupé. The cars were also made available as the S1204 with an 1189 cc version of the engine, which gave 53 bhp at 5100 rpm and increased the top speed up to a very healthy and useful 90 mph.

Top left: a pretty S1300GT, with coachwork by Pietro Frua. This car was first marketed in 1964

Above left: the 1963 Glas 1500 cc saloon

Left: the sister car to the Frua coupé S1300GT, this example being in convertible guise

THE GREAT CARS/Glas

By 1964, entirely new coupé and convertible models were available, with stylish bodies by Frua. These were known as the S1300GT and were complementary to the S1004 which, the company decided, should stay in production. The cars featured an improved chassis, with the wheelbase lengthened to 8 feet 7 inches and conventional double-wishbone front suspension. Disc brakes were already standard on the front wheels and the cogged-belt engine was increased in size to 1289 cc with the power up to 75 bhp at 5800 rpm, giving both models a top speed of 105 mph. Also available in 1964 was the 1500, a four door saloon with similar suspension to the 1300GT models but with its wheelbase increased to 9 feet 2½ inches and the familiar engine increased in size to 1492 cc, although the power was kept down to 70 bhp in the interests of improved torque for improved mid-range acceleration.

The seeds of financial trouble to come were sown at this time, for Glas seemed reluctant to drop any model, however unsuccessful, and the range still contained the Goggomobil and Isar models as well as the multitudinous variations on the S1004, 1300 and 1500. Demand for the smaller models had long evaporated in the face of the challenge from Volkswagen and the many other small-car producers, but they stayed in production hopefully.

By 1965, there were both saloon and estate-car variants of the 1004 in the catalogue, both of which were available with the 1289 cc engines as options, while the 1500 had grown into the 1700, the cogged-belt engine now stretched to 1682 cc and the power output raised to 85 bhp at 4800 rpm. Glas claimed a top speed of 100 mph for the 1700, although a British magazine only managed to squeeze 90 mph out of a test example. A TS version with an engine tuned to give 100 bhp at 5500 rpm was also catalogued. This engine was also made available for the 1300 GT coupé and convertible, which were known as the 1700GTs. The 1700 was capable of 115 mph according to Glas, but the 1300 versions remained in production for those with less sporting inclinations.

Not content with this unwieldy range, Glas introduced a big saloon in 1965. This luxury machine was powered by a new V8 engine which was, in effect, two of the four-cylinder engines on a common crankcase, with two separate cogged belts driving the single camshafts on each bank. With a capacity of 2576 cc, this unit represented two of the 1289 cc, four-cylinder units and, using three downdraught Solex carburettors conveniently situated in the vee of the engine, it gave 150 bhp at 4600 rpm.

Although it featured the same wheelbase as the 1700 saloon, the 2600 V8 used a de Dion rear axle in conjunction with semi-elliptic leaf springs. Automatic chassis levelling control by Boge was fitted as standard equipment. Glas claimed a top speed of 124 mph for the 2600 but the expense of putting this £3000 car into production took the company into serious financial trouble by early 1966.

The Glas factory and its assets were taken over by BMW, who themselves had weathered a severe financial storm only four or five years earlier. BMW immediately dropped all the smaller models which were uneconomical and kept only the 1700GT and 2600V8 in production. They fitted their own 1600 cc, four-cylinder engine into the 1700GT and also grafted their trailing-arm independent rear suspension onto some models. The 1700GT was renamed the 1600GT but it lasted in production only a short while and, by 1969, the name of Glas had been erased from the BMW catalogues. MT

Right: the 1965 Glas 1700

Below: the company took a major step in 1965 by introducing a new V8 series; the cars were technically highly advanced but, as happened with the Borgward company, the models could not save the firm

Above: one of the last cars the company built, the 1304CL of 1968

Right: an estate version of the 1304CL, which was available with a 1289 cc engine

Glassfibre/HOW IT WORKS

BODYWORK FOR THE SPECIALIST

A number of advantages, as far as car production is concerned, have made glassfibre a popular alternative to steel

Above: steel and other metals are not common on low-volume-production car bodies, due to the high cost of making tools for the manufacturing process. Glassfibre is an ideal substitute—especially since it does not rust. It is possible to colour the glassfibre rather than painting it, but most manufacturers, such as Reliant with their Robin, prefer paint; apart from any other considerations, it is almost impossible to touch-up any damaged areas on a colour-impregnated body

CAR DESIGNERS HAVE CHERISHED AN AMBITION for many years of being able to build a car body entirely of plastics, instead of the expensive and complicated steels which require tooling costing millions of pounds and then begin to rust away as soon as they are on the road. The ultimate ambition is merely to squirt some plastic material into a mould and form a complete car body. This has been done experimentally, but had not, by 1974, been developed to production standards.

The majority of mass-produced cars have used steel chassis and body units, and those smaller manufacturers who could not afford the tooling for steel bodies have traditionally been obliged to use such materials as aluminium, wood or fabric. These materials all have serious drawbacks such as lack of strength, rapid deterioration and a tendency towards rotting, so car makers have always been searching for an alternative.

Plastics first came under consideration before World War II when Ford began an investigation in the USA, and the Henry Kaiser firm built some experimental sports models soon after the war. These were doomed to failure because the plastics materials used were simply not good enough. However, the advent of polyester resins and glassfibre mat in the early 1950s opened the door to the commercial use of plastics in car building.

The materials developed in the 1950s were still in use in the 1970s, and were largely unchanged, although much development had taken place to improve quality. The basic material of the glassfibre car body is a loosely woven mat formed from individual filaments of glass which are held together with a binding material. These mats are available in many different widths, thicknesses and textures according to the use intended. These glassfibre mats are very flexible and have no real strength, but when coated with a polyester resin and a catalyst they become extremely hard and resistant to attacks from acids and other corrosive liquids. Modern glassfibre materials are treated with fire-resistant chemicals which retard the spread of flames in an otherwise highly inflammable material.

The majority of car bodies are made by the hand lay-up method which involves the operatives in painting a mould with a release agent (to prevent the body sticking), painting on the gel coat (to give a smooth, shiny surface), then applying a layer of resin and catalyst hardener, before lining the mould with the glassfibre mat, then coating it with a further layer of resin and catalyst by hand brushing. More layers of glassfibre mat and resin are added, according to the thickness required, then the mould is left to cure under stable heat conditions—usually around 75 degrees centigrade. When the body shell is hardened, it is removed from the mould for trimming, filling and painting.

The major snag with this method is that it is slow and labour intensive, for all the operations have to be carried out by hand, and the mould is out of action until the body is cured. A manufacturer who wants to

HOW IT WORKS/Glassfibre

Above: Reliant workers put the finishing touches to Robin three-wheelers on the production line

Top right: glassfibre is very useful for carrying out repairs to bodywork, be it steel or plastic. Various grades and types of glassfibre matting are available and resin is mixed with hardener before the mat is impregnated

Above right: glassfibre finds extensive use on racing cars. This Lola T332 Formula 5000 car has glassfibre bodywork (the red parts other than the airfoils) built by Specialised Mouldings. These parts give a weight and cost saving over metal, although light alloys are used for the load-bearing parts such as the monocoque

poorly designed and made, but it was the means of putting several firms into the car manufacturing field. A large number of the smaller companies turned to glassfibre, and such firms as Bond, Diva, Deep Sanderson, Elva, Fairthorpe, Gilbern, Ginetta, Gordon-Keeble, Marcos, Reliant, Ogle, Peerless, Rochdale, Tornado, Turner, TVR and Unipower came into being when glassfibre became readily available. In Europe, small firms like Alpine and Matra in France turned to glassfibre for their bodies, as did Sabra in Israel, Otosan in Turkey, Puma in Brazil and a number of other small makers throughout the world.

Two British firms, Rochdale and Lotus, made the first serious attempts to build cars with glassfibre chassis as well as bodies. The main problem with this type of construction is that glassfibre has little inherent strength for carrying a load such as that imparted by suspension members. The Rochdale Olympic was perhaps more successful than the Lotus Elite because it had a very thick chassis to which metal plates were bonded, but the company lacked the resources to build a large quantity of bodies must have numerous moulds, taking up a good deal of space. The process is also very messy and smelly, so the factory tends to be a rather unattractive place to work, with the result that labour turnover is very high. Generally speaking, the hand lay-up process is not suitable for production quantities of more than fifty cars a week.

The first production car to be built in glassfibre was the Chevrolet Corvette which first appeared in 1953. Chevrolet were not too certain about the demand for an American-built sports car so, rather than build it in steel at great expense, they built the first models in glassfibre by the hand lay-up method. Demand soon outpaced this slow process, and Chevrolet were eventually forced to build metal dies. With metal tooling, over 30,000 bodies a year can be built. The advantages of metal dies are that accuracy can be held to closer tolerances and curing takes only a matter of minutes, against several hours for the hand lay-up method. The Corvette is built at the rate of around 25,000 cars a year and, although panel fit and quality have been criticised, there are undoubtedly a higher proportion of early Corvettes still in service than metal cars of an equivalent age.

In Britain, the earliest use of glassfibre in the motoring field was in the supply of body shells for fitting to Ford and Austin specials. Most of these bodies were develop the car fully. The Lotus Elite suffered from failures when suspension components tore through or away from the glassfibre chassis. Since then, the Clan Crusader has been built largely from glassfibre, but it too suffered from fatigue failures, although the company went out of business for different reasons.

Two British companies of some size, Daimler and Jensen, built car bodies in glassfibre over a considerable period. Daimler used the material for their SP250 sports model, making the bodies by the hand lay-up method in their Coventry works. The body suffered from a rather ugly shape and from the fact that the chassis was insufficiently rigid, with the result that doors tended to fly open on corners! Jensen built their 541 and CV8 models from glassfibre over a long period, only turning back to steel when they developed their unit-construction Interceptor model.

As well as complete bodies, many manufacturers build components in glassfibre; there is a thriving business in glassfibre hardtops, many steel-bodied cars having glassfibre tops as optional extras. Accessory firms also supply glassfibre door, boot, bonnet and wing panels to replace rusted or accident-damaged steel panels, while a number of racing saloon models have glassfibre panels in place of the standard steel units in order to save weight. The beach-buggy era also saw extensive use of glassfibre.

793

Glassfibre/HOW IT WORKS

Right: a partly built Lola T360 Formula Atlantic car, showing the glassfibre top section (orange) fixed to the alloy monocoque

Far right: the cockpit-section master mould. It is from this that the glassfibre mould is made

Below: Reliant Robin bodies on the production line after painting

Glassfibre has revolutionised the racing-car industry. Until the early 1950s, racing cars were usually clothed in aluminium bodies, laboriously handmade at some expense, with many of the parts as permanent fixtures to the chassis. With the arrival of glassfibre, manufacturers were able to make many bodies from the same moulds, using panels which could be held in place by spring clips or other fasteners. The glassfibre panels do not dent easily like aluminium, can be quickly repaired in the event of an accident and can easily be modified by bonding new parts to existing panels. A complete new industry has evolved around glassfibre, and such firms as Specialised Mouldings devote all their time to designing and building glassfibre bodies for racing cars. One company, Ginetta Cars, even went so far as to build a Formula Three racing car using a monocoque chassis built from glassfibre, but it proved to be insufficiently rigid.

Although many companies now use glassfibre bodies, the big breakthrough into mass production is yet to come and this will not happen until injection moulding techniques are perfected, for even the metal-die method used on the Chevrolet Corvette requires a good deal of handwork, since the glassfibre mat must still be placed in the die by hand and the resin sprayed over the mat before the die is closed. However, with increasing steel prices, there is evidence to suggest that interest in glassfibre is increasing, although resin prices rose dramatically during the oil crisis.

The great advantages of glassfibre, such as its almost total resistance to corrosion of any sort, its ability to be impregnated with the body colour desired and its ease of repair, are all much sought after by engineers. It was originally thought that glassfibre bodies would be less safe in a crash than steel ones, but it has been found that a properly designed glassfibre body is as effective in a crash as a steel body. The panels tend to tear badly in accidents, where a steel body crumples, but it is easy to cut out the torn sections and bond in new ones. Glassfibre repair kits are now used almost universally to repair rusted or accident-damaged steel cars because of the material's cheapness and ease of use.

A number of glassfibre-bodied cars such as the Reliant Scimitar, Ginetta G21, TVR and the four-seater Lotus Elite have all passed the obligatory crash tests to meet EEC requirements, so the material will meet safety requirements into the 1980s and, with further curtailment expected in steel production, it seems that glassfibre-reinforced plastics have a long life ahead of them. MT

THE GREAT CARS/Gobron-Brillié

THE FIRST 100 MPH MOTOR CAR

The name of Gobron-Brillié will live forever in the motoring books as the first motor car to achieve the magic 100 mph. The record was set in July 1904

Above left: the first Gobron-Brillié cars, which appeared in 1898, had the engine mounted at the rear in a triangulated tubular chassis.

Above: the engine fitted to the original Gobron-Brillié was a vertical twin, producing 8 bhp

Left: the 1898 Gobron-Brillié with double phaeton bodywork

IT IS FOR ITS PERFORMANCE rather than the excellence of its construction that the Gobron-Brillié is remembered, for it was a racer built by this company that was the first car to exceed 100 mph.

Like all the cars to leave the company's works at 13, quai de Boulougne, Boulougne-sur-Seine, near Paris, the racer had an opposed-piston engine of distinctive design. The Gobron-Brillié engine usually had its cylinders cast in pairs, with the two lower pistons acting on a common crank throw; at 180 degrees to this were two secondary throws linked by long, thin connecting rods to a crosshead above the cylinders. The second pair of cylinders was mounted on the crosshead, their stroke being slightly shorter than that of the lower pair to compensate for the extra weight of the linkage. The valves and sparking plugs were located halfway down the cylinders, with the explosion taking place between the pistons. Inlet valves were initially automatic, then mechanically operated, with inlet on one side of the bore, exhaust on the other (which called for the use of two camshafts). Finally, and logically, both sets of valves were lined up neatly on the same side of the cylinders. This design feature meant that only one camshaft was necessary.

So why the duplicated piston arrangement? A French journalist summed it up in 1903: 'For the same swept volume, the system of bringing the pistons together to act by pushing one against the other, results in a stronger compression. Without this method, it would be essential to allow for extreme stresses in the cylinder bore'. And, as Gobron owners have testified, the *Système Gobron* also resulted in a smoothness of running that was rare in veteran days.

It is easy to see that the stroke of the engine was obtained by combining the distances travelled by both pistons, but the ever-suspicious British taxation authorities obviously believed that the whole was greater than the sum of the parts, for they devised a fiendishly complex method for calculating the taxable horsepower rating of opposed-piston cars.

Another distinctive feature of the early Gobrons was a revolving petrol distribution device which replaced the carburettor. The quantity of fuel passing into this apparatus could be regulated by a drip-feed device, so that the Gobron-Brillié cars could run on a wide variety of fuels apart from petrol. Even, claimed

Gobron-Brillié / THE GREAT CARS

the company, pure alcohol, benzene, or any good spirit, such as gin, brandy or whisky.

The first Gobron-Brillié cars, which appeared in 1898, had the engine mounted at the rear in a triangulated tubular chassis which was typical of the make. This arrangement, it was claimed, gave parallel drive and an engine that was easy to get at from all sides. *Phaeton, char-a-banc, wagonette* or *duc-tonneau* bodies were available on this 8 hp twin Gobron although, by 1901, it was being supplanted by a front-engined model with three-speed epicyclic transmission with, apparently, equal speeds both forwards and backwards, though what purpose could be served by reversing at 55 kph in top gear was not explained. Chassis price was Fr 7000.

The front-engined cars were available with twin-cylinder engines of 8, 12, 14 or 16 hp; these could be doubled up to four cylinders if extra power was required. Gobron-Brilliés were also built under licence in France as La Nancéenne, and in Belgium as the Gobron-Nagant.

Gobrons and Nancéennes ran in the 1901 Paris-Berlin race, while in the Circuit du Nord alcohol-fuel contest that year, Rigolly's Gobron took third place. The next year, he won his class in the Château-Thierry hill climb and the Circuit des Ardennes, again using alcohol. It was a prelude to the most famous Gobron-Brilliés of all, a team of three cars built for the Paris-Madrid race, all with 13·5-litre four-cylinder engines. The bore was 140 mm and the two pistons had unequal travels of 108 and 112 mm, resulting in an aggregate stroke of 220 mm. The cars, driven by Rigolly, Duray and Koechlin, did not fare particularly well in the Paris-Madrid (which was, in any case, halted by Government edict at Bordeaux because of the many accidents *en route*), but subsequently, in speed hill-climbs and sprints, the cars proved virtually invincible. There were victories at the Castlewellan hill-climb held in conjunction with the 1903 Gordon-Bennett, at the Ostende speed meeting, at Grenoble, Laffrey, Château-Thierry and Dourdan.

'The marque which from one day to the next has confirmed itself queen of speed can be legitimately proud of these triumphant results', eulogised Georges Lefevre, recording Duray's 136 kph victory at Dourdan. 'They do not know any more what it is to be beaten: everywhere they take the first place'.

On 17 July 1904, Rigolly, whose car had been over-bored to 15 litres, took part in the Ostende Automobile Week, averaging 103·56 mph over the flying kilometre,

Below: on 17 July 1904, M. Rigolly, driving a 15-litre Gobron-Brillié racer, took part in the Ostende Automobile Week, averaging 103.56 mph over the flying kilometre. This was the first time that the magic 100 mph had been reached, thus ensuring the Gobron-Brillié a permanent place in the history of motoring

THE GREAT CARS/Gobron-Brillié

In the spring of 1907, a small fleet of the new 40/60s was put into service by the Westminster Bridge Garage, operating a London-Paris run from the Ritz in London to the Ritz in Paris in 15 minutes under 12 hours, going out on the Friday to return on the Monday. The trial run was recorded for posterity by a bioscope operator; the total cost of the round trip was 12 guineas.

Gobrons featured prominently in another hire scheme of the period, this time operated by Automobiles De Luxe of Islington, who offered 60/75 Gobrons for £6 6 shillings daily (up to 120 miles).

The big Gobrons had an ingenious double-cone clutch to ease the load on the transmission; first, a small, metal-to-metal cone began to take up the drive, then a massive fabric-lined cone bit home. There were also twin foot-brakes with separate pedals, acting on drums either side of the four-speed transmission housing. While engaging, the starting handle automatically slid a half-compression device into operation, thus easing the load of the labouring chassis faced with swinging all those pistons into life.

For 1908, Gobron announced a 15/20 four, with shaft drive, priced at £500 in chassis form; the big six had now become a 70/90, and cost £1600. However, an

Top: the giant Gobron-Brillié 40/60 hp of 1906. It was fitted with a four-cylinder motor of 7.5-litre capacity and was capable of nearly 70 mph

Above: a 1913 20 hp Sporting tourer, with boat-tailed coachwork by Rothschild

the first time that 100 mph had been exceeded (Rigolly and Duray, incidentally, had become the first men to breach the 150 kph barrier four months previously). Nor was this epoch-making piece of ton-up-manship the end of the Gobron racer's history, for it also ran in the 1906 and 1907 French Grands Prix, and was only barred from the 1908 event by a change in the formula governing racing that year.

Meanwhile, at the end of 1903, Eugene Brillié and Gustave Gobron had parted company, Brillié joining the Ateliers Schneider at Le Havre to build cars and commercial vehicles of more conventional design.

Gobron continued with the opposed-piston design for touring vehicles, although by 1904 the fuel distributor had been supplanted by a more conventional carburettor as the result of Duray and Rigolly's work in tuning the racers for maximum speed, and chassis were now pressed steel.

The archetypal Gobron-Brilliés were big, powerful, chain-driven touring cars—in 1906, the company listed a four-cylinder 24/35 hp, a 7.6-litre 40/60 hp four and a monstrous 60/75 hp six, with over 11 litres under the bonnet. This cost £1320 as a bare chassis, and the other models were proportionately expensive and just as well made.

automatic starter was now part of the equipment.

A couple of years later, there was a 12/16 hp twin, priced at only £300, though British sales seem to have been centred on the 15/20 and 20/30 hp fours. The last of the giant Gobrons was produced in 1910 and thereafter the marque seems to have gone into a gentle decline, more markedly so after World War I in a new factory at Levallois-Perret.

The last of the opposed-piston cars appeared in 1922: this was the 25 hp, which seems to have been intended as an exercise in sheer perversity, for it combined the two-piston-per-cylinder layout with sleeve valves, camshaft braking and triple carburettors. Hardly surprising, it was in production for less than a year, and thereafter all was convention, with a 1·5-litre engine supplied by Chapuis-Dornier. It sold badly, and even an attempt to disguise it as a Stabilia failed to ameliorate the situation.

The last of the Gobrons was a supercharged 1·5-litre side valve sports car, which won the 1500 cc class in the Six Hours of Burgundy race, driven by its designer, Chabreiron. It also won its class in the 1930 *Circuit des Routes Pavées*, but the victory was also an epitaph, for in 1930, Automobiles Gobron ceased production.   DBW

Golden Arrow/WORLD OF SPEED

THE RECORD-BREAKER THAT RAN ONLY ONCE

Sir Henry Segrave and the Golden Arrow are immortal in motor-sporting history. Ironically, during its entire active career, Golden Arrow covered less than thirty miles

WORLD OF SPEED/Golden Arrow

Below right: Major Sir Henry Segrave receives a diploma from the Founder of the 'Automobile Club de France' in Paris in October 1929. Handing over the diploma is Baron Zuylen De Nyevelt De Haar who was also celebrating 25 years as President of the club

THE WORLD LAND-SPEED RECORD was held, in 1929, by Ray Keech, with his monster 81-litre, triple-engined *Triplex Special*. Keech's car was probably the crudest record breaker ever built, and the sort of machine that makes one wonder whether the designer thought that brute force in the end would overcome the need for aerodynamics.

The car that was due to take the 207.55 mph record from Keech was a revelation. It was streamlined, smooth and looked the part of a record-breaking car, rather than an over-powered monster. The fact that the car could play the part, as well as look it, was justly proved when, in March 1929, Major Henry Segrave took the car to a speed of 231.45 mph; all on a 'mere' 23.9 litres of single W12 Napier Lion engine. The *Golden Arrow* (named after the Arrow-configuration engine and the gold aluminium coachwork) was designed by ex-Sunbeam engineer J. S. Irving and the body was built by Thrupp and Maberley. The car's engine had a capacity of 23,970 cc and it produced 900 bhp. Segrave's earlier car, the Sunbeam *Slug*, which took the record, at 203.79 mph in March 1927, produced 1000 bhp, again proving the efficiency of the Golden Arrow shape. The car's slab sides housed cooling surfaces for the engine: if the water in the engine boiled, ice chests built into the bodywork would make contact with the coolant, the procedure being controlled by a thermostat device.

Segrave took *Golden Arrow* to Daytona in March of 1929 and with just one practice run behind him, set out for the 1 mile record. The car was equipped with a telescopic sight mounted on the long bonnet. The idea of the sight was that the driver could use it to aim at a centre point at the end of the run, and so not running diagonally. On 11 March, the car took the record at 231.45 mph—with consummate ease. Two days after the successful attempt, the *Triplex Special* was brought out again, this time in the hands of Lee Bible. Unfortunately, the car went out of control at 200 mph and turned over throwing the driver out; *Triplex Special* careered on and killed a photographer who was standing at the end of the run. Segrave, who was knighted later that year, decided to give up land-record attempts for the time being, after the fatal crash and turned his attentions to the water-speed record. On 13 June in the following year, 1930, Segrave was attempting the world record on Lake Windermere in the Lake District when his craft, Miss England II, struck a log and capsized, killing the pilot. This meant that after one record run, the *Golden Arrow* had to be retired. It is now on display at the National Motor Museum in Beaulieu, Hampshire. LJC

The Wild Bull from the Pampas

Above: Froilan Gonzales poses with the 1950 World Champion, Nino Farina

Left: Gonzales in action at Silverstone during 1951, driving the 4.5-litre Ferrari

JOSE FROILAN GONZALES was one of the most popular and talented of the bunch of South American drivers who invaded the European motor-racing scene in the 1950s. He never matched the almost clinical tidiness of his countryman Juan Manuel Fangio, because his technique at the wheel of a racing car was to hurl it at every corner as fast as it would possibly go, sorting out the slides with lightning movements of his enormous arms.

Like Fangio, Gonzalez, who was born in 1922, raced the primitive cars used in Argentinian road races, but these powerful old cars with poor roadholding helped him to achieve a great deal of skill in controlling slides on the dirt roads often used in local races. The Argentinian Government under President Peron was amiably disposed towards motor racing in the late 1940s and early 1950s, so in 1950 Gonzalez was given the opportunity to join Fangio in Europe. He was given a drive in the Scuderia Argentina team of 4CLT Maseratis, taking the place of Fangio, who had gone to the works Alfa Romeo team. He soon showed his skill, with a heat victory in the Albi GP and second overall on total time.

In early 1951 he returned to Argentina for the early-season races, taking a 2-litre Ferrari to Buenos Aires, where he gained the ecstatic admiration of his countrymen by beating the pre-war 1939 blown 3-litre Mercedes-Benz Grand Prix cars, although the German cars were by no means running well.

Back in Europe he drove one of the big 4½-litre Talbots in the Paris GP, where he finished second, and he also drove a sports version at Le Mans, with his countryman Onofre Marimon, but they retired. He was offered a place in the Ferrari team of 4½-litre Formula One cars later in the season, when Taruffi was taken ill, and in his first race, the French GP at Reims, he was holding second place when he was obliged to hand over to his team leader Ascari.

He stayed with Ferrari for the rest of the 1951 season, winning his first Grande Epreuve at Silverstone when he won the British GP after an initial battle with Fangio's Alfa Romeo. This spirited drive earned Gonzalez the affection of the British motor-racing public who christened him the Pampas Bull, because of his 18-stone figure and his hard-driving tactics.

He took third place in the German GP, followed by second places at Barcelona and Monza, and finished third in the World Championship, behind Fangio and Ascari. He also took second place at Bari and at Modena in a Formula Two race.

For 1952 Gonzalez was signed by Maserati to drive their 2-litre car in World Championship races; he had little luck against the rapid Ferraris and he preferred to blow up his engine rather than finish in a low position. His only placing of note was a second at the Italian GP. He also handled the 1½-litre BRMs in races at Silverstone, Albi and Goodwood and put up some brave performances in these difficult cars, with a couple of minor wins at Goodwood to his credit. He also drove the Thinwall Special to victory at Goodwood. Gonzales stayed with Maserati for 1953 but again he played second fiddle to the Ferraris, although he took third places in the Argentine, Dutch and French GPs and fourth in the British GP. Another brave display in the Albi GP with a V16 BRM almost brought victory, but tyre failure caused him to settle for second place.

With the coming of the 2½-litre Formula One in 1954, he joined the Ferrari team. This change brought him more success, for he won the British GP again—his second and final GP win—and finished second at the German and Swiss GPs, third in the Argentinian and Italian GPs and fourth in the Belgian GP. His British GP win at Silverstone was taken at the expense of countryman Fangio in the all-conquering new Mercedes 'Silver Arrow', so his victory was all the more popular in Britain. He took second place in the World Championship for 1954 and also won the Le Mans 24-hour race in a 4.9 Ferrari, co-driving with Maurice Trintignant. He was none too successful in long-distance sports-car races because he tended to break the cars rather quickly.

His career was interrupted by a bad crash during practice for the 1954 TT race at Dundrod in a 3-litre Ferrari. He had a broken shoulder and other injuries and decided to retire from racing, but he took part in the Argentine GP of 1955, sharing the third placed Ferrari with Farina and Trintignant. However, he decided not to come to Europe for the remainder of the 1955 season and restricted himself to local events. He drove a 3-litre Maserati with Jean Behra into third place in the 1956 Buenos Aires 1,000 km. race and was temporarily lured back to Europe later in the year to drive a Vanwall at his favourite circuit—Silverstone. The car broke its transmission at the start, however, and he went back to Argentina never to return.

From then on Gonzales took part only in South American events, usually with a Chevrolet engined Ferrari, but he did enter the 1957 Argentinian GP, where he drove a Ferrari with the Marquis de Portago, finishing fifth.

The burly Argentinian gradually eased himself out of racing to concentrate on his garage business. There is little doubt that he would have won far more races and probably taken the 1954 World Championship, had it not been for the skill of Juan Manuel Fangio. MT

THE RISE AND FALL OF GOODWOOD

AFTER WORLD WAR II, Britain's two major motor-racing circuits, Brooklands and Donington Park, were in a serious state of disrepair. The Brooklands track had been severely cut about by its wartime use for aircraft construction and maintenance, and Donington was used as an Army depot. Neither circuit was in a state to be raced on again and the necessary finance to rebuild them was not forthcoming.

However, there were several ready made circuits laying idle all over the country, for the military airfields vacated at the cessation of hostilities all had suitable perimeter tracks which could be used for racing. One of these airfields was the Westhampnett fighter base near Chichester in Sussex which happened to have been built on the estate of the Duke of Richmond and Gordon, who also owned the Goodwood horse-racing course nearby. In pre-war days, the

Below: for a number of years, Goodwood was the scene of the famous Tourist Trophy races. This picture shows a Ferrari 250GTO during practice for the 1963 TT event

Goodwood/WORLD OF SPEED

Right: an aerial view of the Goodwood circuit. As can be seen, the area surrounding the track is extremely flat; the circuit was, in fact, originally an airfield

Duke, then the Earl of March, had been a prominent racing driver, even building his own cars, the March Specials, so he was enthusiastic about the possibility of using the airfield as a race track as soon as World War II came to an end.

Work was started in 1946 and, after some resurfacing and demolition of military buildings, the track was opened on 18 September 1948. Reg Parnell won the Goodwood Trophy in his Maserati at the opening meeting and Dennis Poore won the Woodcote Cup in his Alfa Romeo. The circuit was received enthusiastically by both drivers and spectators alike and the British Automobile Racing Club (successors to the Brooklands Automobile Racing Club) adopted the track as their home circuit now that Brooklands was denied to them.

Above: the notorious Goodwood chicane. Many a driver has been caught out by the severity of this artificial obstacle. Here a Lister-Bristol successfully negotiates the chicane during a meeting in 1954

The track was 2.38 miles (3.83 km) long and featured several interesting corners which drivers found challenging. From the start, a short straight led into the tricky right-handed Madgwick corner which had a double apex, causing drivers a great many heart-stopping moments. From Madgwick, a short straight led to the long Fordwater bend which curved to the right and could be taken by the brave at over 140 mph. Hard braking was then required for the tricky right-left kink at St Mary's, which was followed almost immediately by the tight right-handed Lavant corner. The Lavant straight which followed was not really a straight as it had a left-handed curve at the beginning and a right-handed kink at the end just before Woodcote corner, a 90 mph right-hander which led back along the straight past the pits.

The circuit became popular because it was pleasantly situated close to the South Downs and was an easy drive from London. It had none of the artificial flavour of Silverstone or Snetterton because it was a grass airfield so the infield was all grass or cultivated. It developed some of the Brooklands atmosphere of 'the right crowd and no crowding' because the more affluent motor-racing supporters tended to flock to the Goodwood circuit.

Gradually, the BARC built up permanent stands opposite the pits and earth banks round the outside of the track, so that spectators were able to view the racing easily. In 1952, an artificial chicane was placed on the track just before the pit area; this brick chicane became infamous because of the damage it caused to cars that were unfortunate enough to collide with it.

Two large stands were erected by the chicane and these became a popular meeting place for BARC members who came to watch the fun. A snag with the circuit was that the infield could only be reached by driving across the circuit, which meant opening the track after every race to allow people to enter and leave, but the BARC eventually overcame this problem by building a tunnel.

Although the circuit did not have the spectator capacity to host the British Grand Prix, a number of major races were held at Goodwood including the Goodwood Nine Hour race and the Tourist Trophy, while the traditional opening meeting of the season was the Formula One Easter Monday meeting.

After a number of accidents at the Dundrod circuit, the Tourist Trophy was transferred to Goodwood for

WORLD OF SPEED/Goodwood

Above: another view of the chicane. Here a Ferrari leads a Porsche Spyder and two Lotus machines during the 1959 Tourist Trophy

Left: the start of the 1963 TT, showing a couple of Ferraris leading an assorted field of sports and grand-touring cars. From the start line, a short straight leads into the tricky, double-apex, right-handed Madgwick, a corner which has caused many drivers anxious moments

the 1958 season where the 4-hour race was won by the Aston Martin of Stirling Moss and Tony Brooks. Moss also shared the winning Aston Martin the following year; he took over Jack Fairman's car when his own caught fire at the pits. The TT dropped out of the World Sports Car Championship in 1960 and did not return until 1964 when it was run over 130 laps of the Goodwood circuit; it resulted in a win for Graham Hill's 4-litre Ferrari. The TT moved to Oulton Park for the 1965 season.

Perhaps the most famous of all the races held at Goodwood were the Goodwood Nine Hour races which were an attempt to recreate the atmosphere of the long-distance Brooklands races such as the 200 mile race and the Double 12. The first Nine Hour race was won by Peter Collins and Pat Griffiths in an Aston Martin, ahead of a pair of Ferraris. In 1953, it was Aston Martin again, the winning DB3S being driven by Reg Parnell and Eric Thompson, who only took the lead when the works Jaguars retired. The Goodwood circuit was criticised at the time for its very abrasive surface, for Dunlop changed no less than 300 tyres during the nine hours. Peter Walker and Dennis Poore completed a hat trick for Aston Martin when they won the 1955 Nine Hours from the Titterington/Sanderson D-type Jaguar. With their Le Mans starts, fuel and tyre stops, these races were an exciting change from the usual run of club races held at Goodwood most weekends.

Several drivers made their names at Goodwood, the most notable being Mike Hawthorn, who lived only a few miles away at Farnham. He started racing in a Riley, then moved to a Cooper-Bristol with which he defeated many well known drivers, earning himself places in works teams. Another driver who came to the fore at Goodwood was Tony Brooks, who raced borrowed Healey Silverstones and other production sports cars with such verve that he was snapped up by Connaught before being signed by Vanwall, Ferrari and finally BRM.

Stirling Moss also performed extremely well at Goodwood, winning a number of Formula One races as well as taking the TT four times in succession, but the circuit was responsible for bringing his career to an end when he left the track on the fast Fordwater bend at the Easter Monday meeting in 1962. Moss was driving a Lotus-Climax V8 and, having made a pit stop with gear selection trouble, was running three laps behind the leader, but still racing at lap-record speeds. Suddenly, his car veered off onto the grass bordering the outside of the track and crashed head-on into the bank. Moss received severe head injuries which effectively ended his racing career. The reason for Stirling's accident has never been fully explained.

In 1965, with the coming of a 3-litre Formula One for 1966, the Duke of Richmond and Gordon announced that he would be closing the track for good because he felt that the speeds attained by the 3-litre cars could easily lead to a serious accident involving the public. However, it would have been relatively inexpensive to improve the already good earth barriers at the circuit and it was felt by many people in motor racing that the main factors in the closing of the circuit were the increasing complaints from nearby householders about the noise level, and the Duke's own loss of interest in motor racing. The loss of the track was keenly felt in the south of England because it left only Brands Hatch and the under-utilised Castle Combe and Lydden Hill circuits as the remaining tracks in the south. However, the British Automobile Racing Club who were now without a home circuit eventually took over the Thruxton circuit near Andover in Hampshire.

The final meeting at Goodwood in 1966 was for Formula Two cars when Jack Brabham won in a Brabham-Honda at 99.51 mph. The official lap record was left at 1 min. 20.4 secs by Jim Clark (Lotus-Climax V8) and Jackie Stewart (BRM V8), an average speed of 107.46 mph.

Strangely enough, the circuit was kept open for private testing, although many of the facilities were removed. The McLaren team used the track for testing their Formula One and Can-Am cars and it was during one of these private test sessions that Bruce McLaren was killed in June 1970 while testing a Can-Am McLaren. The circuit is still open for private testing sessions.

MT

Gordini / THE WORLD OF SPEED

THE FRENCH CALL HIM 'LE SORCIER'

ALMOST SINGLE-HANDED, Amédée Gordini upheld the honour of France in motor racing throughout the two decades after World War II. Despite severe financial difficulties, he managed to field cars in most of the Formula One, Formula Two and sports-car classics until the final demise of his racing-car concern in 1957 when he concentrated on a Renault tuning business which was to prove highly successful in the following years, not only with competition results but with modified road cars.

Gordini was born near Bologna in Italy in 1899 and, after leaving school, was apprenticed to a Fiat dealer; he later joined Isotta-Fraschini, then went to France for an extended holiday. Legend has it that he spent his fare home during a riotous party and was obliged to remain in France. However, the more probable explanation was that he had met an attractive French girl. Whatever the reason, he married the girl and remained in France where he set up in business in 1926 to maintain and tune the many Fiats which were both imported, and also built in France by Simca.

Business flourished and in 1929, Gordini took up competition driving, taking part mostly in rallies, until 1935 when he took up motor racing. He did well in events like the Bol d'Or, a 24-hour race, and also won the Rudge Whitworth Cup at Le Mans in 1939. For most of these events he used special-bodied, highly-modified versions of the Fiat 508C and 508S models. His successes were noted by the Simca directors and he was given some help in building his cars. When the war ended, Simca offered much more assistance, both financial and material, and Equipe Gordini was set up to build competition cars. It was decided that single-seaters would gain more publicity for Simca than modified saloons, so Gordini built a single-seater using almost all Simca components. With a simple twin-tube chassis, independent front suspension by wishbones and a live rear axle with torsion bars, the chassis was both light and strong, since the car scaled little more than 7 cwt. It was powered by a Simca-Fiat 1100 cc push-rod ohv engine tuned to give around 65 bhp which gave it a top speed in excess of 110 mph. The car gained a number of minor successes and for 1947, the engine size was increased to 1220 cc and the power output went up to 100 bhp. The French ace Jean-Pierre Wimille began to race the Simca-Gordini and was soon putting up some fine performances, winning at Nimes and finishing second at Lausanne, while other drivers won at Reims and the Bol d'Or. The little cars came up against Formula One machinery during the season, the drivers finding much to their surprise that they were very competitive. Raymond Sommer finished second in the Albi GP to Rosier's Talbot and Wimille finished second in the Nice GP to Villoresi's Maserati.

This encouraged Gordini to increase engine size for 1948, so the faithful Simca-Fiat engine was considerably modified, being enlarged to 1430 cc and fitted with a new cylinder head featuring cross-over pushrods, similar to those used on the BMW. This engine, which gave 105 bhp enabled Gordini drivers to pick up many minor successes in 1948. A new central-seater sports car also appeared, picking up a number of class wins in long-distance races. The young Maurice Trintignant won the Formula Two Perpignan GP in 1948 while in 1949 Fangio drove a Simca-Gordini to victory in the Marseilles GP.

Gordini realised that his victories were gained mainly because of his car's light weight and knew that once his rivals gained sufficient power he would not be able to hold them, so he persuaded the Simca directors to allow him to build a 1½-litre, Wade-supercharged, twin-overhead-camshaft engine. With dimensions of 78 × 78 mm, this 1496 cc engine gave around 115 bhp and, although it was installed in an almost unchanged chassis, it was good enough to win the Albi GP for Trintignant, while the same driver drove a road-equipped coupé to second place in the Liège–Rome–Liège rally.

The relatively minor wins and placings did not please Gordini who felt that he could do well in Formula One. However, Simca were reluctant to increase their financial support with the result that the cars got worse instead of better. The split between Gordini and Simca came to a head when all four Simca-Gordinis blew up their engines in the 1951 Le Mans race and the agreement between Gordini and Simca was rapidly ended.

Gordini had already earned the nickname of 'Le Sorcier' because of his supposed wizardry at extracting high power outputs from mundane engines, so he found no difficulty in obtaining a backer. He quickly designed a 2-litre version of the 1½-litre Simca-Gordini unit, this being a six-cylinder engine with dimensions of 75 × 75 mm, for a capacity of 1987 cc. With three Weber carburettors, this engine was claimed to give 175 bhp but its subsequent performances showed that this was rather optimistic. A

Above: shortly after World War II, Amédée Gordini built his first single seater. The car was powered by an 1100 cc ohv Simca engine, tuned to give around 65 bhp. Later the engine size was increased to 1220 cc

Near right, top to bottom: the Gordini Formula Two car of 1952. This was fitted with an in-line six-cylinder engine of 2 litres capacity, which produced 155 bhp at 6000 rpm;

the 1955 Formula One Gordini in action at the Argentine Grand Prix

Prince Bira of Thailand tried the 1952 F2 car during a demonstration at the 1974 French Grand Prix

WORLD OF SPEED / Gordini

Below right: 'Le Sorcier', Amédée Gordini, pictured in his workshop

completely new tubular-steel chassis with torsion bar independent front suspension and a torsion-bar sprung live rear-axle was devised for F2 racing and, as the World Championship was for F2 cars in 1952, the tiny Gordini equipe tackled the Championship with cars for Jean Behra, Maurice Trintignant and Robert Manzon. Behra took third place at the Swiss GP, Manzon had a third in the European GP at Spa, Manzon and Trintignant were fourth and fifth in the French GP, Behra was fifth at the German GP and Manzon was fifth at the Dutch GP. Manzon also won the sports car Monaco GP in a sports 1½-litre model and Behra won the Reims GP. The cars were rather unreliable however, suffering from rear axle failures on numerous occasions and Gordini's slender resources were stretched to their limits, and beyond, towards the end of the season.

Gordini was not a designer but a gifted mechanic who could improvise on the spot, but what the team needed was an engineer who could design from scratch rather than bodging up production parts. Gordini refused to take on a designer with the result that unreliability and lack of performance dogged the team to the end.

For 1953, the cars remained much as before but were even less competitive than the previous year, picking up odd fifth or sixth places in Championship events and the only victories of any note were Trintignant's wins at Chimay and Cadours, while Fangio took third place in the Bordeaux GP.

Gordini fielded a new coupé for Le Mans. This was powered by an enlarged version of the F2 engine, which was bored out to 2½-litres. Driven by Trintignant and Schell, the car went reliably, taking sixth place at an average speed of 102.45 mph. Things were looking up, for the 1954 Formula One was to be for 2½-litre engines. As well as the bigger six-cylinder engine, Gordini built a straight-eight 2982 cc unit with the same 78 × 78 mm dimensions of his 1½-litre unit. The 4 gear-driven twin-overhead camshafts and hemispherical combustion chambers followed previous designs and, with four Weber carburettors and a 10.8:1 compression ratio, the engine gave 235 bhp. It was fitted to a sports car for Le Mans and Reims but handling problems caused it to be withdrawn at both of the races.

The 2½-litre, six-cylinder engine was utilised for the 1954 Formula One and, although Behra won the Pau GP early in the season, the team quickly deteriorated. The car still retained a live rear axle and had little more than 210 bhp against the sophisticated chassis and 270 bhp of the all-conquering Mercedes-Benz cars. A few minor placings were picked up in World Championship races, and Behra took second place in the Daily Express Trophy at Silverstone, third in the Bari GP and third in the Caen GP, while he won the Cadours race. The sports cars fared a little better in 1954 with a number of good placings in minor races plus an overall victory for Pollet/Gauthier in the Tour de France with a 2½-litre sports model. Pollet and Guelfi took sixth place at Le Mans with a 'six' but the 'eight' in the hands of Behra/Simon had trouble with

its new Messier disc brakes. However, Jean Behra won the Coupe du Salon at the Montlhéry circuit at the end of the season.

The Gordini team started the 1955 F1 season with the old six, but by mid season a new straight eight car was ready. This engine, derived from the 3-litre unit had dimensions of 75 × 70 mm for a capacity of 2498 cc. Four twin-choke Solex carburettors replaced the Webers from the 3-litre, and the 2½ was supposed to give 255 bhp at 7300 rpm which would have made it competitive, but it probably had no more than 230 bhp. It was mated to a new 5-speed gearbox, independent suspension was utilised on all four wheels and Messier disc brakes were fitted all round, inboard at the rear. Clothed in a sleek all-enveloping body, the eight-cylinder looked attractive. It did not make its début until the Italian GP in September but, driven by Jean Lucas, it lasted only a few laps.

In the meantime, the old six-cylinder cars had been pressed back into use but the only places of any note were a fifth at Bordeaux, seventh at Monaco for Pollet and seventh at Aintree for Mike Sparken.

For the 1956 season, Gordini intended to run a pair of eight-cylinder cars in Grand Prix races but they were again unreliable and suffered from poor handling so the old sixes were brought out again from time to time. With one of the old cars, Robert Manzon surprised everyone by winning the Naples GP while Andre Simon took a second place at Caen. The eight-cylinder racers went from disaster to disaster, either crashing in practice or running miserably slowly at the tail of the field. Their only victory was in a minor event at Montlhéry when da Sila Ramos won the Autumn Cup—against a motley collection of relatively uncompetitive sports cars.

The sports cars fared little better. Even a new 1½-litre four-cylinder, twin camshaft engine could not get class wins, while the bigger cars invariably retired from the long-distance races.

For 1957, a new six-cylinder Formula Two engine

Top left: a modified F2 car that Gordini was forced to use in F1

Top centre: an R8 Gordini on the 1966 Tour de Corse

Top right: one of the first R8s, of 1964

Above: the 1952 Le Mans 2300 cc sport

Above right: the 1954 Le Mans car, this time with a 2½-litre engine

Right: a Renault 12 1600 Gordini

WORLD OF SPEED / Gordini

was announced, but it never appeared, and the team relied on the old eight and six-cylinder cars once again. Da Silva Ramos finished sixth at the Pau GP with an eight and then took a six to Naples where he retired. It was painfully obvious that unless more capital and engineering know-how was injected, Gordini would struggle on in the same old way but, before the season was very old, the state-owned Renault factory offered him the job of developing their production cars. He gladly accepted and quickly closed down his Paris workshops to concentrate on his newly-appointed task.

Renault realised only too well the value of competition victory as a sales booster, while the name Gordini meant a great deal to the French motorist, so Gordini was set to work modifying the Dauphine, bringing the power output up from 26 to 38 bhp. With various other modifications, the car was sold under the name Dauphine-Gordini. Over the next few years, these cars did well in competition, among the events they won were the Monte Carlo rally and the Tour of Corsica in 1958.

When the new Renault R8 appeared in 1964, Gordini also designed a modified version. It, too, did quite well in competitions and a National Championship was run for R8 Gordini's, but priority was gradually switched to the small Alpine concern of Jean Redélé who built rapid little sports cars at Dieppe. Gordini designed a twin-camshaft version of the Renault engine which did well in Alpine and Réné Bonnet sports cars but, when Alpine fitted it to a Formula Two single-seater, its 110 bhp was no match for the 140 bhp Honda unit used by Brabham. In 1968 Gordini devised a V8 engine which was effectively two of his 1500 Renault-Gordini units on a common crankcase. It was used in the Alpine A220 but it lacked performance and was eventually dropped from the catalogues.

One of Gordini's later projects was the Renault R12 Gordini, a tuned version of the front-wheel-drive saloon but in 1974, at the age of 75, Amédée Gordini has little close association with the modified cars which bear his name, the work being done by a team of specialist Renault engineers. However, it is a wonderful testimony to the affection in which he is held that his name is still used by Renault some 17 years after a Gordini car last took part in a race.

MT

Gordon Bennett Cup/WORLD OF SPEED

FORERUNNER OF THE GRAND PRIX

The Gordon Bennet cup series was a fiasco, but it is remembered in motor-racing history because the collapse of the event led to the introduction of Grand Prix racing

Above: Selwyn Francis Edge waits with a slightly steaming, four-cylinder, 13,700 cc 80 hp Napier. Edge, who won the 1902 event, had bad luck here in 1903, when his car came last. The 1903 race was won by Camille Jenatzy in a 60 hp Mercedes

IF IT HADN'T BEEN for James Gordon Bennett, one of the most famous sayings of all time—'Dr Livingstone, I presume?'—would never have made the dictionary of quotations. For it was Gordon Bennett, Paris-based proprietor of the *New York Herald*, who financed H. M. Stanley's expedition to look for the lost Livingstone. He was the kind of newspaper magnate who made news rather than waiting for it to happen.

Gordon Bennett's income enabled him to live very well indeed, whether in his château at Versailles or aboard his 2000-ton steam yacht, *Lysistrata* and it was while he was cruising in the Mediterranean in 1899 that he conceived the idea of a challenge cup for motor racing. Bennett had been a motoring enthusiast since 1893, had formed part of the committee which was the nucleus of the Automobile Club de France, and had done much to further the cause of motoring through his editorial columns. In consultation with the ACF, Gordon Bennett drew up the rules for his race.

Commented the Parisian *International Motor Review*: 'At the time he offered the cup, France had so completely monopolised the industry that other countries seemed to be incapable of building satisfactory cars, to say nothing of competing with the French in their own races. Mr Bennett was well aware that the time was not far distant when France would find her monopoly threatened. He wanted to encourage foreign countries to enter upon this struggle, and also provide a means of showing the progress they were making by instituting an annual contest. To make the comparison a fair one, he offered the cup with the stipulation that the vehicles competing were to be built throughout in the countries they represented. He also desired that the trophy should be known as the International Challenge Cup'. Needless to say, it soon became known as the Gordon Bennett Cup.

The prize was to be raced for only by official representatives of clubs recognised by the ACF, so the Automobile Clubs of America, Austria, Belgium, Germany, Great Britain & Ireland, Switzerland and Turin were all eligible to enter a team limited to three cars and three drivers. However, the race, held on 14 June 1900, turned out to be something of a fiasco, for, apart from the three French cars, there were only single entries from America, Belgium and Germany— Winton (Winton), Jenatzy (Bolide) and Eugen Benz (Benz). The three French cars were all Panhards, their drivers—De Knyff, Charron and Girardot—chosen by ballot, a move which had caused much ill-feeling, for the Mors drivers who had done so well in the races of the past season were permitted only reserve status.

Moreover, it proved almost impossible to obtain official sanction for the race, which was to be held over 354 miles of public roads from Paris to Lyon. Suddenly, the race was on, at 24 hours' notice. Benz protested that his car wasn't ready, and refused to start; Jenatzy only took part after much persuasion.

Because of the uncertainty, less than 200 people turned up to watch the start from the Montretout level crossing of the Versailles road; apart from the five official starters, Levegh (Mors) was running *en amateur* in the hope of winning and thus registering his protest against not having been chosen for the French team.

'If the start was inauspicious,' complained *International Motor Review*, 'the race itself was utterly devoid of interest.'

Winton retired when one of his wheels collapsed and Jenatzy lost his way due to the lack of organization, got off the road and wandered about the country before retiring at Gien.

'What with car troubles, obstreperous gendarmes, dogs and flocks of sheep, I have never in my life driven such a race', he moaned.

De Knyff stripped all the teeth off his top gear, Girardot lost his way and damaged his steering, and Charron, having bent his back axle, was about to retire when he learned that he was the only one left in the race. So he carried on, his mechanic, Fournier (who later became a well-known driver in his own right) pouring oil over the straining driving chains. Despite a spectacular collision with a St Bernard ten miles from the finish, which sent the car off the road,

WORLD OF SPEED / Gordon Bennett Cup

across a ditch, through a field and back onto the road facing the way it had come, Charron finished, watched by a handful of sightseers. Only five of the official reception committee had bothered to wait for him, and competitors and officials then adjourned to the nearest cafe, joined by Levegh, who had arrived—unofficially—second, and Girardot, who had managed to patch his steering gear together.

If the first Gordon Bennett was a fiasco, the second was a total disaster. The French manufacturers cared little for the event, the outside world even less. De Knyff stood down, and the French team consisted of Charron and Girardot on 24 hp Panhards, plus Levegh on a 50 hp Mors, 'the most powerful car that had ever taken part in a race'. There was only one foreign challenge, and that a last-minute one: it came from Napier, who had built a monstrous 50 hp car for S. F. Edge. Mercedes would have entered, but preferred to concentrate their efforts on the Paris–Berlin race. Because of the lack of entries, the Gordon Bennett was combined with the Paris–Bordeaux race. Edge was disqualified before the race started, because the Dunlop tyres fitted to his car gave so much trouble on the way to Paris for the event that he was forced to change them for French tyres. In any case, although he ran in the Paris–Bordeaux, he retired with a

Below left: Cecil Bianchi's 1905 96 hp Wolseley, posing with the Napier racer

Below right: the Honorable C. S. Rolls with the Wolseley racer just before the start of the 1905 race

Above left: Sidney Girling's Wolseley in the 1904 event

Above right: the wrecked remains of Earp's Napier at the British eliminating trials at the Isle of Man for the 1904 event in Hamburg

Left: Algernon Lee Guinness at the wheel of the stubby Weir-Darracq in 1905

broken clutch at Couhé-Verhac. Charron crashed, Levegh retired, and only Girardot finished among the Gordon Bennett entrants: he was ninth.

In 1902, the Gordon Bennett was combined with the Paris–Vienna; again, Edge was the only competitor from overseas, and the French team was arbitrarily chosen as de Knyff (Panhard), Fournier (Mors) and Girardot (CGV). On the first day Fournier broke a gearshaft while racing an express train carrying spectators on a line parallel to the course, while Girardot had already retired with clutch trouble; the third and last day, De Knyff broke his differential crossing the Alps, and dropped out only 30 miles from the finish of the Gordon Bennett, at Innsbruck, leaving the race to Edge.

Though the French had virtually disregarded the Trophy while they held it, once it had been taken from them, it became a matter of supreme importance to win it back.

As the organisation of the race had now passed to the Automobile Club of Great Britain & Ireland, it became necessary to find a suitable course: this was impossible in England because of anti-motoring legislation. However, a bill was passed permitting the

Gordon Bennett Cup

race to be held in Ireland over a roughly figure-of-eight shaped course centred on Athy and Carlow.

For the first time, the Gordon Bennett attracted a worthwhile entry-list: Britain had Edge, Jarrott and Stocks in Napiers, France De Knyff and Henry Farman in Panhards plus Gabriel in a Mors; America sent Mooers (Peerless) and Winton and Owen in Wintons. Mercedes had built six 90 hp racers for the event, but five of these were destroyed in a fire at the Cannstatt factory, so the German team was made up of three borrowed 60 hp touring cars. As the 60 hp Mercedes was a far better car than the 90, this was a fortunate disaster; Jenatzy won the race at the wheel of Clarence Gray Dinsmore's Mercedes, and the massive trophy passed to Germany.

The 1904 Gordon Bennett was contested over a course in the Taunus mountain district of Germany by teams selected from the finest drivers and cars of Britain, Germany, France, Belgium and Italy: a Swiss, Dufaux, did not start. The race was a complete success, and was won by Leon Théry, driving a Richard-Brasier at an average speed of 54.5 mph. Théry's lap-times were a marvel of consistency: out of the four laps of 79.5 miles which made up the distance, he covered three in 1 hour 26 minutes plus between 22.5 and 56.8 seconds, while the odd lap was only three minutes longer.

However, the regulations of the Gordon Bennett Trophy, drawn up to ensure that no nation had the advantage of numbers over its rivals, carried in them the seeds of their own destruction.

France felt that it was getting a raw deal, as its makers were capable of putting far more cars on the starting line than those of any other country. So the ACF proposed a new race, the Grand Prix de l'Automobile Club de France, which they said would be run concurrently with the Gordon Bennett, open to any number of makers from any country. But in deference to opinions like that of the Hon John Scott Montagu—'The Gordon Bennett cup is basically the Blue Riband of motor racing, and it is my opinion that it would be preferable to keep it quite separate from any other race whose aims seem to be more commercial'—the Grand Prix was held over to 1906.

The 1905 Gordon Bennett race took place over four laps of an 85-mile course in the Auvergne, not far from Clermont-Ferrand and the Puy de Dôme. The three level crossings on the circuit were bridged by wooden flyovers so that the racers would not be held up.

The circuit, claimed *La Vie au Grand Air*, was full of difficulties from one end to the other: 'Long hills where the power and cooling systems of the engines will be put to the test; many corners and hairpin bends where the stability and acceleration of the cars, as well as the skill of their drivers, will be tried to the utmost.'

As the French Eliminating Trials to choose the team were held over the Auvergne circuit, it's hardly surprising that the three drivers and cars qualifying for France—Théry (Richard-Brasier), Callois (Richard-Brasier) and Duray (De Diétrich)—occupied the same placings in the event proper. Théry justified his nickname of 'Le Chronomètre' by once again lapping with consistent regularity: M Clémentel, Minister of the Colonies, awarded the unflappable Théry with honorary membership of the Academie Francaise to celebrate his second victory in the Gordon Bennett. But it was also his—or anyone else's—last, for the Trophy was thereafter suspended 'indefinitely' to make way for the first French Grand Prix in 1906.

What was the man who had—if involuntarily—given his name to this first international racing trophy

like? James Gordon Bennett was, it seems, something of an Anglophobe, with an especial dislike of the British Press lords. He was also notably eccentric, with an ungovernable temper which was unleashed on anyone who happened to disagree with him over any matter in which he was interested. For years he insisted that the leader column of his newspaper should carry a letter from 'The Old Lady from Threadneedle Street' inquiring how to translate Centigrade into Fahrenheit; this daily item only ceased when Gordon Bennett died, in 1918.

In spite of his periods of intense hatred of everything and everybody around him, Gordon Bennett was a generous man, who would reward good service with a gold watch or would give a destitute peasant a handful of money.

He is also recorded as having a considerable taste for what Edwardians discreetly termed 'reckless entertainments'. His parties afloat mixed what he called 'the gilt-handled snobs of society' with scantily-clad French and American showgirls: one dinner was terminated by a teenage ballet dancer performing stark naked on the table.

Indeed, one night in 1902 the Princess Schaumberg-Lippe took such exception to a fandancer that she asked to be put ashore at once: the next morning she cut Gordon Bennett dead while strolling along the front at Nice. It was a social snub that became the talk of the French Riviera. And, in typically Gordon Bennett fashion, she was pictured on the front page of the Paris edition of the *New York Herald* the following day, with a caption that was distinctly unflattering to the Princess.
DBW

Top: J. W. Stocks in the queue of cars waiting to be weighed in Ireland before the 1903 event

Above: De La Touloubre's Darracq in the French eliminating trials of 1905

THE GREAT CARS/**Gordon-Keeble**

A LUXURY GRAND TOURER

A striking blend of Anglo-American-Italian motor car design. With power from a Chevrolet, styling by the master hand of Bertone and chassis and building by Gordon-Keeble themselves, the car was said by many to be the simple answer to the question 'What is the complete grand touring car?'

MANY NEW CAR MANUFACTURERS sprang up in the euphoric days of the late 1950s and early 1960s when demand always seemed to outstrip supply and the public would buy almost anything on wheels. It was into such an atmosphere that the Gordon-Keeble was born, but the company planned not to attack the mass market but to go for the well-entrenched specialist manufacturers like Bristol, Jensen and AC. That they failed, but failed gallantly, is one of the tragedies of recent motoring history.

John S. Gordon had previously been managing director of Peerless Cars, who built a Triumph engined four-seater of pleasing proportions. He sold his interest in this company and the Peerless eventually became the short-lived Warwick GT. Gordon had plans for a much more ambitious machine which duly appeared in 1960. The Gordon GT, as it was called, was a large four-seater, with an attractive coupé body designed by Bertone of Italy and power from a big Chevrolet V8 engine. This was by no means the first time the combination of a big, lazy American engine in a European chassis had been tried but, in this case, the specification of the chassis was unusually sophisticated. Designed by Jim Keeble, the car had a multi-tubular steel frame using square-section tubes. At the front, the car used double-wishbone independent suspension in conjunction with coil springs and

Gordon-Keeble/THE GREAT CARS

telescopic dampers while a de Dion rear axle was fitted at the rear. This was located by parallel radius arms and a Watt linkage with suspension by coil springs and telescopic dampers. Girling disc brakes were fitted on all four wheels and steering was by Marles worm and wheel.

The power unit of the first model was a standard 4.6-litre Chevrolet V8 giving about 230 bhp, but more powerful versions, ranging right up to 350 bhp were to be made available. Power was transmitted through a single-plate clutch to a four-speed Warner gearbox and on via a short propeller shaft to the chassis-mounted Salisbury differential. When displayed at a Continental motor show, it attracted a good deal of attention, and is even rumoured to have tempted a plagiarist who copied the body for the Iso Rivolta.

With its steel body, the prototype was too expensive to build in small quantities and the design lay fallow for several years until it was decided to build it with a glassfibre bodyshell. A factory was acquired at Eastleigh near Southampton and production began in January 1964. The bodywork was made by the firm of Williams and Pritchard, the chassis being built up at Eastleigh and the body fitted later. With the passage of time, the 4.6-litre V8 was no longer available, so the basic engine was a 5.3-litre unit with hydraulic tappets, a single four-choke Carter carburettor and a compression ratio of 10.5:1. In this trim, it gave 280 bhp at 5000 rpm and 360 lb ft of torque at 3200 rpm. The Warner gearbox was standard, but a three-speed GM automatic gearbox was an option. The only other major change was an increase in size of the disc brakes to 11.38 in at the front and 11.06 in at the rear, a brake servo being a standard fitment.

The car was now called the Gordon-Keeble GK1 and it was catalogued to sell at the very low price of £2798. Sales began to go well, but the price was not an economic one and in 1965 the price was raised to a more realistic £3626. However, the car required an enormous amount of hand finishing and was still not a money making proposition and in May 1965 the company went into liquidation after around ninety cars had been built.

This was not the end of the Gordon-Keeble because a car-sales company, Harold Smith (Motors) Ltd, who sold quality cars in London, took over the assets of Gordon-Keeble Ltd and announced that production would resume. They were as good as their word for cars soon began to appear once again, the only major difference being yet another higher price tag, this time at £3989. This was later increased to £4058, taking the car into a much more competitive range where it was up against cars like the Aston Martin DB6, Bristol 409, Iso Rivolta and Mercedes-Benz 300SE etc. The design was improved, for the much criticised heating and ventilation was modified to give better cooling, wider 5 in wheels were fitted to take Avon Turbospeed tyres and the gear lever was repositioned nearer to the driver.

Sales continued at a low level into 1967 when the company was acquired by an American called De Bruyne. He started a company called the De Bruyne Motor Car Company Ltd, with headquarters at Newmarket and exhibited the GK1 at the New York Show along with a futuristic new mid-engined car using much of the suspension and other running gear from the GK1. The 5.3-litre engine now gave a claimed 300 bhp and was mated to a five speed ZF gearbox, all of which added to the performance.

Unfortunately, that was the last ever heard of the de Bruyne which faded away without another single car being built.

It seemed that the remaining Gordon-Keebles would gradually disintegrate until they remained a memory but faithful owners retained them and, in the early 1970s, Jim Keeble, who had originally designed the car, set up in business to maintain, overhaul and sell the cars. A remarkable number still existed in 1974 and prices of the better ones began to escalate to the sort of price originally asked for a new one in 1964.

Buyers may feel they are getting a bargain even at those prices for there are still very few four-seater GT cars capable of reaching 140 mph, accelerating from 0–100 mph in 16.6 seconds, handling impeccably and offering a very high standard of luxury. With a practically non-corroding glassfibre body, the remaining cars may well be with us for many more years. MT

Above: one of the total of 99 Gordon-Keebles that were built between early 1964 and late 1966. Underneath the glassfibre body was a multi-tubular space frame with a de Dion rear suspension layout. A Salisbury hypoid-bevel final drive was used, and disc brakes were fitted all round

THE GREAT CARS / Gräf und Stift

THE ROLLS-ROYCE OF AUSTRIA

History records that World War I began as a result of the assassination of Archduke Franz Ferdinand. He was riding in his Gräf und Stift at the time

IF ONE HAD TO LIST the outstanding cars of history, there is little doubt that the Austrian Gräf und Stift would be well towards the top. Not because of what it was—one of Europe's outstanding luxury cars—but because it happened to be present at one of the major turning points of modern civilisation. It was while riding in a Gräf und Stift that the Archduke Franz Ferdinand was assassinated at Sarajevo, the spark that set the world ablaze in the holocaust of World War I.

The origins of the Gräf und Stift were relatively humble: in the 1890s the three brothers Gräf—Karl, Franz and Heinrich—were running a cycle repair business in Vienna. Sometime during that period, they built a voiturette to the design of one Josef Kainz. The car, which had a front-mounted De Dion engine, had the unusual feature of front-wheel drive, with the universal joints inside the enlarged steering pivots. A date of 1895 is often claimed for this car (another date is 1897) but since the power unit was the water-cooled single used first on the De Dion vis-à-vis of 1899, it seems likely that the first Gräf car was not built until 1900.

In any case, it was a one-off, and it was not until Willy Stift, former owner of the Automobilfabrik Celeritas, joined them sometime around 1902 that production began. Their first cars were built especially for Vienna's biggest motor agent, Arnold Spitz, dealer in De Dion Bouton, Benz and Mercedes cars, and were marketed under his name; designer of this new model was racing driver Otto Hieronymus, who later inserted a 40 hp engine in a Spitz chassis, entering this hybrid for the 1903 Semmering hill-climb. A variety of Spitz models were built by Gräf und Stift, with one-, two- and four-cylinder engines of French origin: their 12 hp, 16 hp and 24/30 models were especially noted as vehicles of high-quality, with a useful turn of speed. When the Spitz association was terminated in 1907, Gräf und Stift continued building

Below: the first car to be produced by the three Gräf brothers was this two seater runabout. The car was built some time between 1895 and 1900. The car was fitted with a De Dion engine, driving the front wheels

Gräf und Stift/THE GREAT CARS

the same basic design under their own name.

The car in which Franz Ferdinand and his wife Sophie were assassinated was a 5.8-litre 28/32 hp double phaeton, delivered to the Gräf Harrach on 15 December 1910: power output was, it seems, only 32 bhp, a somewhat alarming level of inefficiency. Edwardian Gräf und Stifts were all four-cylindered, shaft-driven machines, with four-speed gearboxes and power units with T-head cylinders cast in blocks of two and then joined together.

Swept volumes ranged from 4.2 to 10 litres; annual production, if the engine number of the Sarajevo car is anything to go by, seems to have been no more than 100, probably a good deal less.

There were, of course, the token appearances in sporting events which were virtually obligatory for quality cars at that time: Cotourier drove a Gräf und Stift in the Eliminating Trials for the 1907 Kaiserpreis, but failed to qualify, while there were also works entries in the Austrian Alpine Trials.

These sporting excursions were, however, no bar to the marque's acceptance by the octogenarian Emperor Franz Joseph, whose attitude towards motor vehicles was generally one of suspicion and mistrust since one of these infernal machines had run amok at an Army manoeuvre at which he was present. Indeed, until his death in 1916 he rode in virtually no other make of car than a Gräf und Stift. His heir, Karl, continued the tradition, and rode into Swiss exile in his Gräf und Stift when the Austrian Empire collapsed after World War I. Thus the car that had played its part in the event that started the war now acted as pall-bearer to the Holy Roman Empire.

But the loss of their most prestigious customer seems not to have worried Gräf und Stift, for in 1921 they announced a splendid new model which, while retaining all the refinement of its predecessors, threw off their conservatism of design. This was the Type SR4, with an overhead valve six-cylinder engine of 7745 cc, which was capable of developing 110 hp, sufficient to move this impressive car (which scaled 2.5 tons in open tourer form) at 85 mph.

There was even a racing version of this car, developed by Fritz von Solnay, which won the euphoniously named Ecce Homo touring car race from Vienna to Berlin.

Alongside the SR4, however, Gräf und Stift built a more conservative 2-litre model, the VK, which had a four-cylinder sidevalve engine, a cone clutch and a

Top left: The Gräf und Stift 18/32PS of 1907

Top right: the 7.7-litre 110 bhp SR4 of 1922

Above left: the luxury Gräf und Stift S3 coupé-de-ville produced in 1926

THE GREAT CARS / Gräf und Stift

mering hillclimb in 1927, and was well placed in other hill-climbing events. The top speed of this motor car was nearly 100 mph.

The SP5 was succeeded by the most magnificent Gräf und Stift of all—the SP8. This was a logical development of the SP5, but had eight cylinders in line, with a swept volume of just under 6 litres. Built only to individual order, the SP8 weighed virtually three tons ready for the road, yet could equal the performance of the SR4.

Its engine had a block cast from silumin alloy, with iron liners and a cast-iron detachable cylinder head. A silent chain drove the camshaft, and the crankshaft was carried in nine plain bearings: power output was 125 bhp at 3000 rpm.

Mounted in unit with the engine was a four-speed

Above left: the 'Rolls-Royce of Austria', this is the 5.9-litre Gräf und Stift SP8 limousine. It had an in-line eight-cylinder engine producing 125 bhp at 3000 rpm. The car weighed nearly three tons ready for the road. This is a 1936 model

Above right: the elegant Gräf und Stift SP8 Sport Coupé of 1932. The car utilised a four-speed gearbox with steering-mounted gearchange. The wheelbase of the car was 12 ft 4 in long

Left: this Gräf und Stift 5.8-litre 28/32 hp double phaeton of 1910 is the actual car in which the Austrian Archduke Franz Ferdinand was assassinated. This was the incident that sparked off World War I

fixed cylinder head. An updated version, the VK2, appeared in 1926: this had overhead valves (though power output was still only 30 bhp) and Perrot four-wheel-braking.

Fritz von Solnay then built a new racing version of the SR4, with the engine linered down to qualify for the under 5000 cc class; this had the valves operated by a single overhead camshaft, and was translated into production form as the SP5 from 1927 on. Von Solnay's racer made fastest time of day at the Sem-

gearbox, with the gearlever mounted on the steering column, operating the gears with vacuum servo assistance. There was servo assistance, too, for the four-wheel hydraulic brakes.

Syncromesh was fitted to the two upper ratios, and top was a geared-up 'overdrive' ratio. The chassis, carried on semi-elliptic springs all round, had a centralised lubrication system and hydraulic shock absorbers: wheelbase was an arrogant 12 ft 4 in.

It was a car of such elegance and refinement that it was dubbed the 'Rolls of Austria', though the mascot of the Gräf und Stift was a silver lion rather than a silver lady. But the market for luxury bespoke cars was a contracting one, and Gräf und Stift sought to widen their appeal by building popular foreign cars under licence, notably the six-cylinder rear-wheel-drive Citroën; there was also a reworking of the German Ford V-8, marketed as the Gräfford, a venture of some obscurity which failed to warrant even a mention in the official history of Ford's European activities.

But there was a more profitable shot in the Gräf und Stift locker—and had been since 1909—in the shape of commercial vehicles.

The last SP8 was produced in 1938, by which time this once impressive car had acquired an unbecoming Teutonic grossness of appearance: after which Gräf und Stift went over entirely to the manufacture of commercial vehicles. During World War II they built light caterpillar-tracked trucks for the Wehrmacht to the design of their compatriot company, Steyr.

Gräf und Stift made one last foray into car manufacture after the war, building the Jawa-designed Aero Minor under licence. But this utilitarian 615 cc saloon was somewhat of a blank Czech, and very far removed from the Viennese firm's earlier productions. For the sake of the reputation of the Vienna Rolls, it is as well to record that the Aero episode lasted only from 1949 to 1950, and that thereafter the company returned to commercial vehicles again. DBW

The epitome of a wealthy amateur

Baron Emmanuel de Graffenreid at the wheel of his 1948 Maserati and posing (*top picture*) with Reg Parnell (*centre*) and Peter Whitehead (*right*) after the 1950 Jersey International Road Race in which de Graffenreid finished third

BARON EMMANUEL DE GRAFFENREID is a fine example of the wealthy, independent amateur racing driver whose heyday was in the pre-war and immediate post-war years, long before sponsorship or factory teams offered drivers the chance to become fully professional. Born in Fribourg, Switzerland, de Graffenreid went into the garage trade and, in 1936 he took up racing with a 1½-litre six-cylinder Alfa Romeo. He won his class in his first-ever race at Berne, a victory which encouraged him to go in for something more powerful for the 1937 season. Partnered by an old friend John du Puy, he bought a pair of Maseratis and the two men raced all over Europe, gaining much experience if little success. De Graffenreid kept his 6C Maserati until the war, winning his class at the odd meeting.

Switzerland was neutral during the war and de Graffenreid stayed there, but as soon as hostilities ceased he was itching to get back into racing, so he bought a new four-cylinder Maserati for the 1946 season and teamed up with fellow countrymen Christian Kautz and Basadonna to race it. He picked up a fifth place at the Grand Prix des Nations at Geneva in 1946 and a third place at Lausanne in 1947. In 1948 he finished third in the Monaco GP and also second in the GP des Nations.

The old Maserati was pensioned off in 1949 to be replaced by a 4CLT/48 Maserati which de Graffenreid drove in a loose sort of team with Prince Birabongse 'Bira' of Siam under the patronage of an Argentinian, Enrico Platé. When the drivers went to the same race they would send their cars in one transporter, thus easing transport costs but the drivers would sometimes go their separate ways or even drive other people's cars when the opportunity arose. De Graffenreid's best ever win came in 1949 when he won the British Grand Prix at Silverstone, benefitting from the retirements of Bira and Villoresi. He later admitted that Silverstone was one of his favourite tracks, partly because it was the scene of his only major Grand Prix win and partly because he disliked racing on tracks bordered by trees and other hard objects. He had an instinctive dislike of tracks like Monaco and his own Berne circuit, especially in the wet, because he knew that a mistake would almost certainly mean injury and a very expensive rebuild, which the team could ill afford. Nevertheless he took second places in the Dutch GP, the Swedish GP and the Jersey Road Race.

The 4CLT Maserati was retained for 1950 and he gained a few minor placings, but the highlight of his career was when Alfa Romeo asked him to drive their legendary Type 158 blown 1½-litre Formula One car at the Geneva GP. He finished a good second and was also asked to drive in the 1951 Swiss and Spanish GPs, where he finished fifth and sixth respectively. It must be admitted that Alfa Romeo's interest was not entirely unconnected with the fact that de Graffenreid had been appointed their agent for the Lausanne area in 1950.

Formula One was abandoned in 1952 in favour of the 2-litre Formula Two, so the Platé team redesigned the 4CLT/48 Maserati by shortening the chassis and removing the supercharger. Although his only Grand Epreuve placing was a sixth at the Swiss GP he took several good placings in minor events.

With a new F2 Maserati for 1953 he took on a new lease of life. In World Championship races he was placed sixth in the Dutch GP, fourth in the Belgian, and fifth in the German GP, while in non-Championship events, he won the Syracuse GP, the Eifelrennen at the Nürburgring and both the Freiburg and Ollon-Villars Mountain-climbs. He also won a heat in the International Trophy at Silverstone but jumped the start in heat two and retired when he was penalised by one minute.

In 1954, with a 2½-litre Formula now in being, he fitted a 2½-litre engine to the Maserati and took it and a sports 2-litre Maserati to South America; he finished eighth in the Argentinian GP with the single-seater, but with the sports car he won the Rio de Janeiro GP at Gavea and the São Paulo GP at Interlagos. He did not contest many European races, because he knew the car was outclassed, and in 1955 he retired from racing after finishing third in the Venezuelan GP in a 3-litre Ferrari, behind Fangio and de Portago, and second in the Lisbon GP in a 3-litre sports Maserati.

He retired to his garage business in Lausanne, selling Alfa Romeo and Rolls Royce cars among others, but he made a short return to the track when he drove for the film Such Men Are Dangerous. Although long-retired from racing, de Graffenreid has retained close links with the sport and in recent years has acted as a roving ambassador for the Marlboro cigarette company which sponsors several teams in Formula One racing. MT

THE GREAT CARS/**Graham-Paige**

AMERICAN MOTORING'S AGE OF CHIVALRY

The Graham brothers attempted to inject a spirit of chivalry into the cut-throat world of motor manufacturing. Their campaign succeeded, but their company failed

THE SCENE COULD ALMOST have been taken straight from *The Idylls of the King:* the heavily-timbered banqueting hall, epitomising all that one thinks of as most typical of medieval architecture, was filled with a merry, wassailing throng, gathered to toast three brothers who saw themselves as the last bastions of the ideals of knighthood.

There were, however, some discordant elements in the tableau: for one thing, in place of coat-armour or richly embroidered tabards, the guests seated at the table were clad in sombre business suits; for another, the venue was neither Tintagel nor Camelot, but the Hotel Roosevelt in New York. But the three Graham brothers who were giving the banquet really did regard themselves as the flower of chivalry. They had just taken over the Paige motor company, whose products would henceforward be known as Graham-Paige, and they had decreed that their profiles, clad in an automotive stylist's idealised concept of chain mail hauberk and helmet, should grace the radiators of the new cars.

In the new company, Robert C. Graham was in charge of sales, Joseph B. Graham was president and Ray A. Graham was treasurer; they, and their guests heavyweight boxing champion Gene Tunney and Notre Dame football coach Knute Rockne, told the assembled motor agents of the new 1928 Graham-Paiges—a range of six-cylinder cars priced between $860 and $2110—and then harangued them on the advantages of belonging to the Graham-Paige Legion, which had been formed to bring the ideals of medieval chivalry into modern business practice.

Originally, Joseph, Robert and Ray had built cabs and bodies for Dodge trucks in their factory at Evansville, Indiana, but, growing more ambitious, had concluded a deal with Dodge under which they would build complete trucks bearing the Graham name, but using Dodge engines and running gear. So in 1921 they began manufacture in a factory in Detroit, which they were to outgrow twice over the next three years as demand grew. In 1925, Dodge took a controlling interest in Graham Brothers Trucks; shortly afterwards the brothers sold the rest of their stock to Dodge and bowed out of the company.

In 1927 they returned to motor manufacture by acquiring the Paige-Detroit Motor Company, which had originally been founded in 1908 to produce a somewhat eccentric two-seater roadster with a three-cylinder two-stroke engine. Two years later, conventionality prevailed, and a four-cylinder, four-stroke model replaced the earlier design.

The car's name was simplified to Paige in 1911; the following year the marque was first exported to England, though judging by the bewildering frequency with which the agency changed hands, the car did not enjoy worthwhile sales over here. In 1914 the Paige agency was held by Byron & Co, of Bloemfontein Avenue, Shepherd's Bush, who were offering the

'15 hp' (actual RAC rating 22.8 hp) and the '20 hp' (25.8 hp) Paiges at £260 and £350 respectively. It then passed to Mr Masser-Horniman's Mass Car Company in Notting Hill, who lowered the price and renamed the marque Mass-Paige to conceal the fact that their own make of car, built in France to Masser-Horniman's specification, was going out of production.

In America, business was rather better: the Paige sold in the same price range as such illustrious marques as Hudson, Cadillac, Oldsmobile and Oakland, and by 1916 the company was doing well enough to have installed a conveyor belt on Ford lines in their factory. The cars had acquired a handsome bull-nosed radiator which, in conjunction with well-styled coachwork, earned the Paige the slogan 'The most beautiful car in America'.

Though the Paige was never more than an assembled car, it had a considerable reputation for sporting performance: most exciting of the company's products was the Daytona Speedster of 1921–27, named in commemoration of a 102 mph record run by a stripped car of this type on Daytona Beach.

There was also a cheaper line, the Jewett, named after the Company's president, Henry M. Jewett, who is reported to have said, in 1925: 'The weak and inefficient (car makers) are going: larger production and fewer plants are the tendency.' Last of the old-school Paiges was the 8–85 Straightaway Eight, with a Lycoming engine of 5274 cc: this survived the takeover, and was marketed alongside the new Continental-engined sixes, of 3128, 3666 and 4740 cc, which were remarkable for the completeness of their equipment—

Above: a 1930 Graham-Paige coupé de ville, standing outside the offices of the company's Italian agents. In the previous year, Graham-Paige had achieved its most successful year ever, producing 77,077 vehicles

Graham-Paige/THE GREAT CARS

and, like their predecessors, for their performance. Captain D. M. K. Marendaz, of Marendaz Special fame, who shared the premises occupied by the British Graham-Paige sales company, broke records with a Graham-Paige at Brooklands and Montlhery, and the same car survived as part of the Brooklands scene, endowed with a new racing body, winning the last-ever race in the hands of its owner, G. L. Baker. Another Graham (as the cars became known after 1928) won the 1929 Monte Carlo Rally.

Under the guidance of the three brothers Graham, the Graham-Paige company prospered spectacularly: in 1928 it achieved its highest ever placing in the American sales league, reaching 12th position; the following year, production peaked at 77,077. European demand was, seemingly, sufficient to warrant the opening of an assembly plant in Berlin in 1928; but all this was swept away in the Depression, when few cars were imported, and the company could not even justify the modest expense of a stand at the London Motor Show.

Despite such setbacks, the Graham-Paige company was the only one of the smaller American car producers to ride out the Depression: and 1932 saw the announcement of a new-style-setting range of Blue

Above: this Graham six-cylinder saloon was first exhibited at the 1936 Paris Show

Centre right: the 1929 Graham-Paige model 827 dual-cowl phaeton

Bottom right: a 1930 Graham-Paige two-seater runabout. Note the 'rumble seat' at the back. By 1930 the Graham-Paige range embraced three six-cylinder and two eight-cylinder models

THE GREAT CARS/Graham-Paige

Streak Eights with pontoon wings, vee-shaped grille and narrow windscreen, plus an ingeniously low-slung chassis, with the rear axle slotted through the frame side-members.

The Blue Streak look was widely copied: but it didn't do Graham-Paige's sales much good; the 1932 figures were 7000 lower than the previous year's.

Nevertheless, the company's approach continued to be adventurous—the 1934 range was crowned by the 4350 cc Custom Eight, which had a centrifugal supercharger driven at five times engine speed by the waterpump shaft. This gave 90 mph plus performance and sparkling acceleration: but though the engine was boosted, sales weren't.

At the 1935 Olympia Show, the British agents, Cleverly's Ltd, exhibited the Graham British Special, based on the supercharged eight-cylinder chassis, with various modifications for increased maximum speed and performance, and fitted with an English body more in keeping with English taste. The whole car was equipped for fast touring, and this work was carried out by Bertelli Limited.

Hardly surprisingly, the British Special (available as either a two-door or a four-door saloon, at prices of £685 and £695 respectively) resembled the current Aston Martin, also part of the Bertelli interests. However, the straight-eight was withdrawn from the market the following spring.

From then on, Graham-Paige concentrated entirely on six-cylinder models, the 21.6 hp, 2780 cc Model 74 and the 25.35 hp, 3679 cc Model 74. These were completely restyled for 1936, and the low-priced model was dubbed the Crusader, while the 3.6 litre became the Cavalier. The body dies of the superseded Special Six were sold to Nissan in Japan, who also used Graham cylinder blocks in building their 1937 Model 70, which marked their entry into the big-car market.

A new supercharged six appeared for 1937, characterised by flowing lines; the chassis was used as the basis of the Lammas-Graham, built by Lord Avebury in a little factory at Sunbury-on-Thames. The supercharged Graham power unit was also used in the last Voisin cars, though Gabriel Voisin refused to be associated with this venture, conceived by financiers who had just taken over his company.

By now, it was obvious that the Graham-Paige Corporation was floundering. The 1936 upswing in the American car market as a whole was not reflected in their sales, which were now a quarter of what they had been eight years before.

The 1938 range—all 3.5 litre sixes—helped not at all, even allowing for the contemporary American predilection for tin-meringue styling, for they were surpassingly ugly, with an inward-raked snout that looked like the result of a hit-and-run accident. Performance, especially with the optional Vacumatic gear-shift and overdrive, was electrifying, but the car was in production for only two years.

The company's last fling was even stranger, for the 1940 Graham Hollywood was built with the body dies from the Cord 810/812 series, also used by Hupmobile: in fact, this Graham was patently a thing of shreds and patches, for it used the Hupmobile chassis as well, only the engine being the real McCoy.

There was still hope, though: during the war, Henry J. Kaiser joined the new president of Graham-Paige, Joseph W. Frazer, in a consortium that would undertake mass-production of cars after the end of hostilities. In 1945 they formed the Kaiser-Frazer Company; the company absorbed the Graham-Paige Corporation and the old factory was taken over for production of Kaiser and Frazer cars. DBW

Top: the 1938 range of Graham models were all fitted with 3.5-litre, six-cylinder engines. The ugly styling, however, handicapped sales and was soon changed

Right, from top to bottom: D. M. K. Marendaz driving a six-cylinder Graham-Paige in close company with the Laystall Special during a 100-mile handicap race at Brooklands in 1929;

a six-cylinder, Weymann-bodied Graham-Paige of 1930,

the two-seater, straight-eight Graham-Paige racer of 1929

The flamboyant Mr Indianapolis

ANTHONY 'ANDY' GRANATELLI is one of the most colourful, aggressive and flamboyant personalities to hit the world of motor racing. His all-pervading desire had been to win the Indianapolis 500-mile race ever since 1946, an ambition which was not realised until 1969.

Born in 1923 near Chicago, Andy Granatelli is a member of an Italian immigrant family and, together with his brothers, Vincent and Joseph, became involved in motor racing. They started a company selling tuning equipment and also promoted racing at a Chicago track. Granatelli then took up motor racing himself, driving in the Mid-West hot-rod categories and in 1946 he made his first attempt at the Indianapolis 500 with a Mercury-powered Miller Special. When he crashed during qualifying for the 1948 event he turned away from driving to become a motor-racing entrant.

For many years, Granatelli grappled with the fearsome supercharged Novi V8s but, although they were often very fast, they seldom lasted very long in the race. Even after the European mid-engined cars arrived at 'The Brickyard' in numbers in 1963, Granatelli persisted with the Novis, but he realised that European technology was needed so he asked Britain's Ferguson company to build him a four-wheel-drive chassis to take the Novi engine for the 1964 race. Although the car was fast in practice, Bobby Unser was eliminated in the first lap crash which stopped the race.

Granatelli had used an engine-oil additive called STP during his unsuccessful years with the Novi cars and he later joined the company, being made president in 1963. Sales were running at around 9 million dollars a year when Granatelli took over but in just five years they had risen five-fold to 45 million dollars and were, in 1974, double that figure. Granatelli publicised STP by naming his cars STP Oil Treatment Specials, flooding the tracks with adverts and dressing himself and his whole crew in overalls bedecked with STP badges.

For 1967, Granatelli retained his Novi-Ferguson but also sponsored Jimmy Clark's Lotus-Ford; the Lotus finished second and the Novi 12th, but Granatelli knew that he had to build a rear-engined car for the next season. In fact, he created a sensation by bringing a neat little side-engined car powered by a modified Canadian Pratt and Whitney helicopter turbine engine. Driven by Parnelli Jones, the car was running away with the race when a transmission bearing failed and the car crawled to a stop, being credited with sixth place.

Although the rules were changed for 1968 to reduce the power output of the turbines, Granatelli sponsored a team of Lotuses with the turbine engine suitably modified. With only nine laps to go, one of them, driven by Joe Leonard, was leading, but the fuel-pump drive failed, as it did on team-mate Pollard's car.

For 1969, Granateili made a determined bid for victory, signing Mario Andretti to drive for him and taking no less than three different cars to the race—a Lotus with a turbocharged Ford V8 engine, a four-wheel-drive Ferguson car powered by a Plymouth engine and a Brawner Hawk Ford. Andretti eventually drove the Hawk, picked his way through the field and gave Granatelli the victory for which he had waited 23 years. Andretti drove again in 1970, using a rather uncompetitive McNamara chassis, but he still managed to finish sixth.

With a view to expanding sales of STP products, Granatelli reduced his racing programme in the USA and spread into other markets. He sponsored the works March 701 Formula One cars driven by Chris Amon and Jo Siffert and ran a March for Mario Andretti in selected events. He also sent a team to the 1970/71 Tasman series. None of the ventures was very successful, but the red-painted cars with the STP stickers gained a great deal of publicity. STP again supported the March F1 team in 1971, with the 711 model driven by Ronnie Peterson. This venture was more successful, for Peterson finished second in the World Championship, although he failed to win a major Grand Prix. STP also supported the 1972 March F1 and F2 teams.

Subsequently, STP spread their sponsorship net wider, taking in Formula 5000 and Formula Ford and reducing their commitment in the upper echelons of racing, although STP did sponsor the March of Roger Williamson, who was tragically killed at the Dutch GP in 1973.

In 1974, however, it was announced that Andy Granatelli had lost control of the STP empire, thus ending a remarkable era in American motor racing.

MT

Below: Andy Granatelli, the man who revolutionised American oval-track racing. As President of STP he earned world fame and victory at Indianapolis

WORLD OF SPEED/Grand Prix

MOTOR RACING'S PREMIER CHAMPIONSHIP

Right: the early days—Boillot and the victorious Peugeot at Boulogne during the 1913 French Grand Prix

Below: 59 years later—Chris Amon leads the field at the start of the 1972 French Grand Prix held at Clermont-Ferrand

The Grand Prix series is the ultimate championship in motor racing

THE WORDS GRAND PRIX are simply the French for 'great prize', a title which was first awarded to a motor race in 1901. Prior to that, motor races had names such as Gordon Bennett Cup, Paris–Madrid etc, although the term Grand Prix had been used in many other sports and pastimes, even in such pursuits as flower growing and cake making!

The first Grand Prix of any consequence was the *Grand Prix de l'Automobile Club de France* run in 1906, although some historians now regard various races run since 1895 as French Grands Prix. Certainly, the 1906 race was the first of these races to be given the title

Grand Prix/WORLD OF SPEED

Grand Prix at the time it was run, its predecessors all being town to town races.

For many years, the *Grand Prix de l'Automobile Club de France* was the only Grand Prix on the calendar, so it was simply known as The Grand Prix.

Prior to 1906, many races had been run on a free formula but, for the 1906 Grand Prix, the French stipulated that all competing cars should weigh less than 1007 Kilogrammes. They hoped that this would keep down engine sizes, but competitors got round this by building flimsy chassis and installing huge engines. Panhard came up with engines of 18 litres, but it was the 13-litre Renault of Ssisz which won the race on a triangular road circuit at Le Mans. The race took place

over two days, each lap covering 64 miles; Ssisz managed 12 laps (769.3 miles) at an average speed of 62.88 mph despite countless stops for tyre changes.

The *Automobile Club de France* were now considered the ruling body of world motor racing and in 1907, they instituted a fuel consumption formula for the Grand Prix, which was held at Dieppe. Each car was to be allowed 231 litres of fuel to cover the 10 lap, 477 mile race, which would require them to average at least 9.4 mpg. Felice Nazzaro in a Fiat won the race at 70.61 mph, and at the end, he still had 11 litres (just over 2 gallons) of fuel left, which was not bad for a car with an engine of over 15 litres!

An international conference decided the complicated rules for the 1908 Grand Prix, run at Dieppe again. All cars had to weigh more than 1100 kg with the four-cylinder cars being limited to a maximum cylinder bore of 155 mm and the six-cylinder cars to 127 mm. This had the effect of bringing engine sizes down, but most of them still had engines of 12 or 13 litres. The race resulted in a win for Lautenschlager's Mercedes at 69.06 mph over the 477 miles.

The French had been beaten two years in succession, a defeat that neither the organisers nor the French motor industry liked at all. They decided that there was not much point in holding races for foreigners to win, so the event was abandoned until 1912, although there had been a race in 1911 called the Grand Prix de France for 3-litre cars. The Grand Prix was reinstated in 1912, again at Dieppe, and run this time to a free formula, or Formule Libre. Although there were several 14 and 15-litre engined cars in the race, it was the comparatively small 7.6-litre Peugeot driven by Boillot which won the 2 day, 956 mile, race at 68.45 mph. However, Britain gained some satisfaction, for a trio of Sunbeams racing in the concurrent 3-litre Coupe de l'Auto class finished a well-deserved third, fourth and fifth overall.

The 1913 Grand Prix, run at Amiens, was again for a mixed fuel consumption and weight formula, the cars being allowed 20 litres of fuel for each 100 km, while the cars had to weigh between 800 and 1000 kg.

This brought both engine and cars sizes down dramatically, the largest being the 7-litre Delages. Boillot again won in his Peugeot.

For 1914, an engine capacity limit of $4\frac{1}{2}$ litres unsupercharged was placed on the cars which also had to weigh less than 1100 kg. The result of the race, run at Lyons, was a classic victory for Lautenschlager's Mercedes, who covered the 467 miles at 65.66 mph. A few weeks later, Europe was at war and there was no more international racing until 1921.

After the war, circumstances had changed considerably. France was no longer the dominant country in world motor racing and, in 1922, the *Association Internationale des Automobile Clubs Reconnus* formed a sporting commission to determine the rules for each year's Grand Prix Formula as well as the various other categories. Soon, other countries were running Grand Prix races, for Italy started theirs in 1921, Spain started in 1923, Germany followed in 1926, Monaco in 1929, Belgium in 1931 and Switzerland in 1934. Several of them ran the races to formulae of their own choosing, but gradually it was realised that a standardised formula would enable manufacturers to build a team of cars at the start of a season and run them at the various races throughout Europe.

In 1921, the French and Italian GPs were run to a 3-litre Formula, the French race being won by

Far left: the Alfa Romeo team line up prior to the start of the 1924 European GP

Above left, top to bottom: Goux's Peugeot competing in the 1913 French Grand Prix;

Leon Théry, winner of the 1905 Gordon Bennett Cup;

Poege's Mercedes undergoing a pit stop during the 1908 French GP

Above, top to bottom: Rudolph Caracciola, German champion of the Mercedes team from 1926 to 1939;

George Boillot, official driver for the Peugeot team before World War I;

Felice Nazzaro, one of the finest drivers of his generation, and winner of the 1907 Grand Prix at Dieppe

WORLD OF SPEED/Grand Prix

American driver Jimmy Murphy's Duesenberg, much to everyone's surprise. America had to wait until 1967 for another GP victory for an American car and driver combination—Dan Gurney in his Eagle at the Belgian Grand Prix.

For 1922, a 2-litre formula was introduced with the proviso that cars should have two seats and weigh not less than 650 kg. The idea of the International Sporting Commission was that the formula would breed a type of car closer to the types the public would buy. To some extent they succeeded, but engines became very complicated, for the 2-litre Delage, Bugatti and Sunbeam engines which this formula spawned would hardly be considered outmoded even today.

The 2-litre cars remained in vogue until 1925, although some organisers preferred a Formule Libre or even a full sports-car race instead of the small 2-litre machines. The formula was reduced even further to 1½-litres in 1926 and 1927 but the requirement of having a riding mechanic had been eliminated, although the minimum weight limit was raised to 700 kg. The formula was a failure because few manufacturers bothered to build cars to it; the ultimate farce was the French GP of 1926 at Miramas when only three Bugattis started and one finished.

There was still no agreement on race distance and organisers were left to run races over whatever distance or time they thought fit. Few were run for less than

Below: the start of the 1923 French GP. Note the poor condition of the track surface and the inadequate spectator protection

Above: the 130 bhp Fiat driven by Felice Nazzaro which, in 1907, won the French GP at Dieppe. The car has a 16.2-litre, 4-cylinder engine and chain drive to the rear wheels

WORLD OF SPEED / Grand Prix

Left: one of the most famous GPs of all time is the Monaco Grand Prix. Here Peter Arundell in a Lotus leads Lorenzo Bandini in a Ferrari during the 1964 event

Left, inset: three drivers who between them have won ten world championships, and who must be regarded as the three greatest drivers produced since World War II: Jackie Stewart (in cap), Jim Clark and Juan Manuel Fangio

Above: Jean Behra (Maserati) leads Luigi Musso (Ferrari) during the 1957 Modena Grand Prix

Above right: Jackie Stewart, later to win the World Championship three times, wheels his BRM around the tricky Monaco circuit during the 1965 GP

Right: 1972 World Champion, Brazil's Emerson Fittipaldi, drives his Texaco-Marlboro McLaren M23 to tenth place in the 1974 Argentine GP

500 km (311 miles) and quite a number, such as the Italian GP at Monza, were invariably run over 800 km (500 miles). This called for several tyre and refuelling stops, while driver changes were permissible between team members.

The 1½-litre Formula petered out in 1928 and most race organisers ran their events for whatever they felt would bring in the largest number of entries and biggest crowd. The French even ran their race for sports cars at one time.

Racing fell into the doldrums in the early 1930s for there was no agreement on what formula to adopt. Some used a fuel consumption formula but most races were run to Formule Libre rules, because organisers objected to the AIACR proposal of a 5-litre formula with a sliding scale of minimum weights.

Then, for 1934, the famous 750 kg formula was announced. This called for a maximum weight of 750 kg and no other restrictions of any consequence apart from body width. For the first time, an obligatory race distance of 500 km (311 miles) was decreed. The International Sporting Commission had reckoned without the state-assisted Mercedes-Benz and Auto Union firms in Germany, who produced fantastically powerful engines for this formula. They swept everything before them in a dazzling display of speed and, although organisers disliked the total dominance of the Germans, they had to admit that the crowds flocked to see the incredible 600 horsepower, 200 mph silver monsters.

The French decided they did not want the Germans winning on their soil in 1936 and 1937, so they held the French GP for sports cars, while the Mercedes and Auto Unions triumphed elsewhere.

For 1938, it was decided that a general lowering of speeds was necessary so the formula was changed to one of 3 litres supercharged or 4½ litres unsupercharged. It was felt that the German teams would not want the expense of building entirely new cars, but both Mercedes and Auto Union built blown 3-litre cars and, once again, swept all opposition off the tracks in 1938 and 1939.

World War II intervened, and when racing restarted, the AIACR was renamed the *Federation Internationale de l'Automobile* (FIA) and a new sporting commission the *Commission Sportive Internationale* (CSI) was formed. The CSI soon decided that the growth of motor racing required a number of different formulae to cater for all the many drivers who wished to take up racing, and the Grand Prix Formula was renamed

Grand Prix /WORLD OF SPEED

WORLD OF SPEED / Grand Prix

Formula One, with the former Voiturette Formula now known as Formula Two. Later, the 500 cc Formula was turned into Formula Three.

The first post-war Formula One was for 1½ litres supercharged and 4½ litres unsupercharged, a formula which saw first of all the dominance of Alfa Romeo's type 158 and 159, then the 4½-litre Ferrari. With Alfa Romeo's withdrawal at the end of 1951, few organisers relished the prospect of a Ferrari walkover in every race, so for 1952 and 1953, races were run to the current 2-litre Formula Two. This provided some good close racing so, for the 1954 season, the CSI introduced a formula for 2½ litres unsupercharged or 750 cc supercharged. This formula provided fine racing right through to 1960 although, in 1958, special racing fuels were barred and all engines had to use commercially available petrol.

By the end of this formula, the rear-engined car was in control, the size of cars had diminished tremendously and race distance had been slashed so that cars could go right through a race without a pit stop. Driver changes during a race were eventually banned and, for many people, the excitement went out of motor racing utterly and completely.

The CSI was becoming concerned at the high speeds being reached by Formula One cars and for 1961, they reduced the engine capacity to 1½ litres unsupercharged. This change brought about a great furore in the racing world and for a time, the British insisted on running their own Inter-Continental formula, but they soon capitulated and eventually dominated the 1½-litre formula with the Coventry Climax and BRM V8 engines.

For 1966, the current 1974 formula was introduced. This was for 3 litres unsupercharged, 1½ litres supercharged with a maximum number of cylinders of 12. The formula also allows gas turbine and rotary-piston engines to compete and the minimum weight was 575 kg. The increasing complexity of the cars called for an immense number of rules on chassis construction, fire-extinguisher equipment, aerodynamic aids etc.

Once again, the wheel has turned full circle, for organisers and drivers are concerned about speeds, the fire risk, which has taken so many lives in recent years, and the need for greater safety in motor racing. With the current Grand Prix formula due to end in December 1975, there is no way of forecasting which way motor racing will go in the future. Certainly, there are those who feel that today's short 195 mile, 1½-hour Formula One races are hardly deserving of the title 'Great Prize' bestowed on that 769.3 miles *Grand Prix de l'Automobile Club de France* in 1906. MT

Opposite page: the start of the 1970 Austrian Grand Prix at the Österreiching circuit; Clay Regazzoni's Ferrari takes the lead from Jochen Rindt in his Lotus 72 and the eventual winner, Jacky Ickx, in his Ferrari

Top left: another scene from the Austrian Grand Prix, this being the 1973 event. Here, the Surtees of Carlos Pace leads the Tyrrell of François Cevert

Centre left: two John Player Special Lotus 72s, driven by Ronnie Peterson and Emerson Fittipaldi, lead a gaggle of cars during the 1973 Swedish Grand Prix

Below: the start of the 1974 British Grand Prix at Brands Hatch. Ronnie Peterson's Lotus 72 shares the front row with pole-position winner Niki Lauda's Ferrari. The winner of the event was car number three, the blue Tyrrell 007 of South Africa's Jody Scheckter

Gravity / HOW IT WORKS

TOWARDS THE CENTRE OF THE EARTH

When the apple fell on Newton's head, he discovered the force of gravity. Today, his discovery plays an important part in the design of the modern motor car

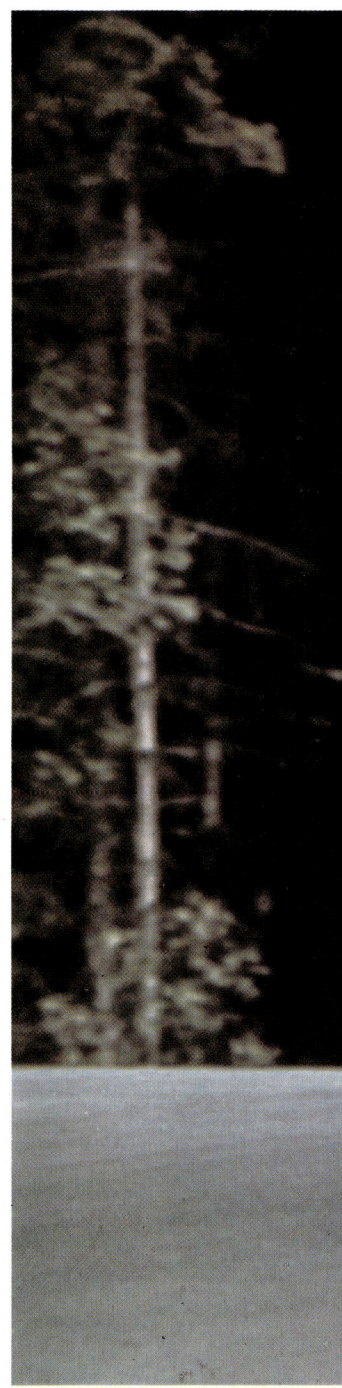

THE FALL OF A BODY TOWARDS THE GROUND is merely the most familiar example of the acceleration of one body towards another, occasioned by the attraction between bodies that we call gravity. Mere weightiness or heaviness is no more than a measure of the force of this pull: when we say that a certain car weighs 2000 lb, we mean that the attraction between the car and the earth produces a pull (acting equally on each, although the earth is substantial enough not to be measurably disturbed) between them of 2000 lbf or pounds force. This pull is resisted by the car's springs and tyres, which are compressed until they summon a total opposing force of 2000 lbf. Drive the car fast over a hump-backed bridge and you may succeed in getting all the tyres just clear of the road, with the springs fully extended. At that instant, the car is weightless, for the upward velocity negates the downward gravitational effect, and there is no force acting to compress the springs nor to keep the driver in his seat or the oil in the sump. An instant later, the car, subjected to the earth's gravitational pull, accelerates downwards (or falls) at the rate of 32.16 feet per second per second. If you drove the car not over a bridge but over a precipice, it would fall 16.08 feet in its first second of freedom, at the end of which its downward velocity would be 32.16 feet per second. After another second, it would have fallen a further 48.24 feet and reached 64.32 ft/sec, and so on. This acceleration is represented in mathematics by the symbol g, and is amenable to all the usual operations of multiplication and so on: $0.6g$ is 19.3 ft/sec/sec, for instance.

Having established g as a measure of acceleration, we can apply it usefully in all directions, not merely downwards. Suppose the grip of the tyres on the road were capable of dealing with a tractive effort of 2000 lbf (produced by an engine torque of 136 lb ft multiplied by a bottom gear ratio of 4:1 and an axle ratio of 4:1,

and applied through tyres of 13 inch radius, to give a simplified example), your 2000 lb car would accelerate at a rate of $1g$, and if it could sustain this it would reach 30 mph in 30 ft. Realising that there was a hazard ahead you might do a crash stop, and if the braking force were 2000 lbf, the car would decelerate (as most decent modern cars can) at $1g$—or accelerate at $-1g$, which is the same thing. However, if you judged there was not sufficient room (ie, 30 ft) in which to stop, you might instead take evasive action by turning right through 90 degrees; if your car could corner at $1g$ (which very few cars can), you might, without altering speed, complete the manoeuvre in 1.37 seconds, by which time the car would be on the point of striking the kerb 30 feet to the right of your original line of travel. The springs and tyres would cushion the blow, so that instead of being jarred upwards instantaneously by the 3-inch kerb, the jolt might be spread over an eighth of a second: the car will be subjected to an upwards acceleration of $1g$.

Clearly, g is a useful tool for the automobile engineer. It enables him to calculate the stresses in components, such as the bending loads on the chassis during your $1g$ bump; it also enables him to work out where the petrol and oil and water and all the other fluids go when the car is cornering, or the amount of squat and dive when accelerating and braking. For these and many other purposes, he may need to know through what notional point the forces involved may be deemed to act: he will want to know the position of the 'centre of gravity'. To calculate it is possible (and in the design stage an approximation at least is essential), but it is tedious; to measure it in the completed car is easy, given some means of tilting the vehicle.

The centre of gravity of a car is located by three coordinates or dimensional references, in the longitudinal, lateral and vertical planes. The first is related

Above left: the lower the centre of gravity, then the smaller the weight transfer effect during cornering. Most saloon cars have fairly high centres of gravity, and this causes severe problems for the suspension geometry which, in turn, reduces the car's cornering power and handling capabilities. Here, the car's mass, acting through the centre of gravity, tries to turn the car over about its roll centre

HOW IT WORKS / Gravity

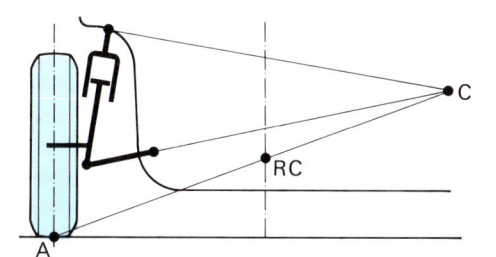

Finding the roll centre of a car: on most modern cars, a suspension system comprising wishbones, or an equivalent linkage, is used. One extends the centre lines of these linkages until they converge (C), then draw a line from that point to the contact point of the tyre (A); where that line crosses the car's centre line will be the roll centre (RC)

to the distribution of weight on the front and rear wheels respectively: if this should be equal, the centre of gravity will be at exactly mid-wheelbase, whereas if the distribution of weight were 45% front and 55% rear the centre of gravity would be further back, 55 inches behind the front hubs of a car with a 100-inch wheelbase. Laterally, the same techniques may be applied, but cars are usually built fairly symmetrically about a longitudinal centre line, and it is unlikely that the centre of gravity will be far from the middle. However, the disposition of load can materially affect the centre of gravity position in a very light car, and there have been cases of essentially sporting two-seaters (the Lotus 11, for example) which were deliberately asymmetrical in construction and springing because the driver would not usually be accompanied by a passenger.

The height of the centre of gravity is more difficult to find, but it is no less important: all other things being equal, the lower the angle of elevation of the

Above: Hans Stuck Jnr on his way to breaking the eight minute barrier at the Nürburgring in his BMW CSL which is temporarily weightless. The car has just hit one of the notorious 'Ring humps and is airborne. For a fraction of a second, the upward velocity of the jolt negates the force of gravity acting on the car. However, status quo is soon restored, and the car will accelerate back to terra firma at the rate of $1g$

Gravity/HOW IT WORKS

Right: Andy Rouse's battered Capri on two wheels at the TT race at Silverstone, 1973. Again, having a fairly high centre of gravity, the saloon leans over, but, the hard suspension of the outside wheels causes the inside wheels to be lifted off the ground

Below: when braked, the inertia of the car (F) is equal to the braking force of the tyres (Tf and Tr). Also, there is a couple about the centre of gravity (G) which is equal to Fh. This transfers weight to the front of the car, and, whether the car has suspension (1) or not (2), the force acting on the front and rear wheels (Wf and Wr) will be the same, except that in the case of the rigid car, the body will be forced to do the work normally done by the springs

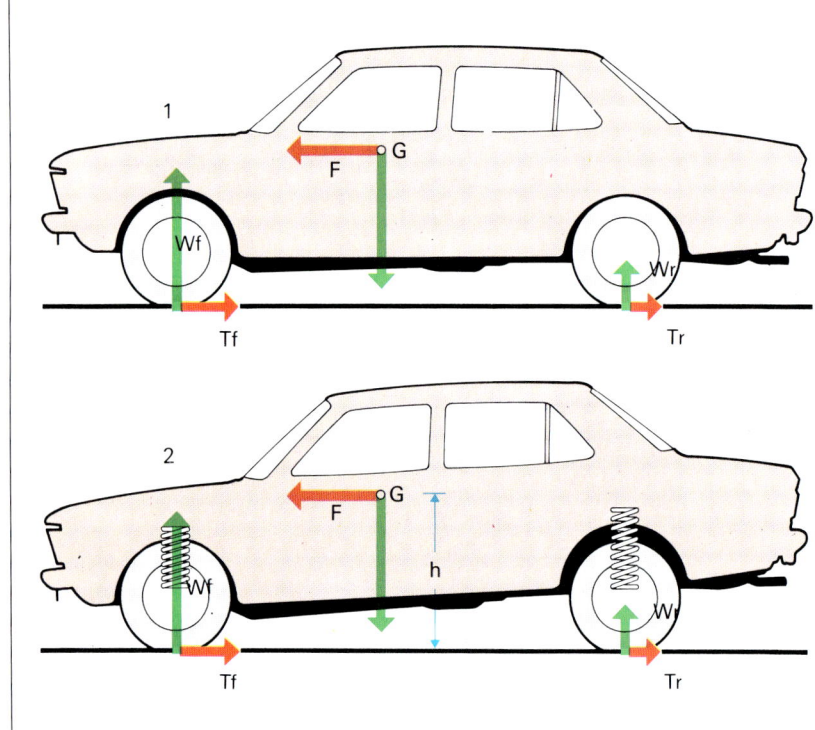

centre of gravity as subtended at the tyre/road interface, the greater will be the stability and cornering ability of the car. Moreover, the height of the centre of gravity above (very rarely below, except in live-axled sports cars of a certain vintage) the roll axis or line joining the front and rear instantaneous roll centres (the points about which the body should roll when cornering), will determine the roll couple during cornering, and thus will have a profound influence on the vehicle's handling characteristics—more profound than the front/rear distribution of weight.

What the centre of gravity cannot tell us is whether all the weight is concentrated in one region or is spread about, perhaps at the extremities of the car. This aspect of mass distribution involves calculation or measurement of moments of inertia, and radii of gyration, which in theory involves multiplying the mass of each elementary particle by the square of its distance from the axis and adding the sum together. The importance of such matters may be understood by considering a pendulum, a dumb-bell and a solid ball. Each item will display very different inertial effects when swung. In engineering the ride and handling of a car, the simple centre of gravity serves for first approximations, but with an important distinction: in yaw, the centre of gravity of the whole car is used, but in pitch and roll and bounce, it is the centre of gravity of the sprung mass which matters. LJKS

WORLD OF SPEED/GRD

RISE OF THE PHOENIX

From the ashes of Lotus Racing Ltd, rose another successful racing company called Group Racing Developments

GROUP RACING DEVELOPMENTS is one of Britain's youngest racing-car manufacturers, having been formed towards the end of 1971, but is already providing race-winning cars in a number of categories.

The company came into being mainly because Lotus decided to withdraw from the manufacture of racing cars for sale to the public. They closed down Lotus Racing Ltd, the subsidiary which built customer racing cars, leaving a number of skilled mechanics without a job. The Managing Director of Lotus Racing Ltd was Mike Warner, who resigned from his position in mid-1971. Although the terms of Warner's contract with Lotus forbade him taking an active part in any other company building racing cars, he was working behind the scenes to organise the former Lotus staff into a new company. First of all, Gordon Huckle, an ex-Lotus Formula One mechanic, formed Group Racing Services to maintain racing cars. Then, in September 1971, Group Racing Developments was formed, with premises at Griston, Norfolk. Former McLaren designer Jo Marquart joined the firm, as did ex-Lotus man Derek Wild. GRD adopted as its badge a Phoenix rising from the ashes, a wry comment on the closure of Lotus Racing.

The company wasted little time in designing and building a racing car and in October 1971, their prototype Formula Three car made its début at Brands Hatch, driven by Andy Sutcliffe. The first design utilised a fairly straightforward monocoque chassis, with side-mounted radiators and orthodox indepen-

Below: Pedro Passadore driving the DART racing team's GRD 373, leads a March 733 during a Formula Three race in 1973

GRD/WORLD OF SPEED

dent suspension on all four wheels, together with disc brakes all round. The chassis was designed as a multi-purpose unit which could be used for Formula Three, Formula Two, Formula Atlantic and the American Formula B. The good showing of the car towards the end of 1971 and early in 1972, when it won an F3 race for the first time, ensured that orders flowed in. The company delivered over thirty cars in the early part of 1972; these were mainly for F3, but there were several F2, FB and Atlantic cars. In Formula Three, the GRD 372 was raced by customers like Tony Brise and his brother Tim, Neil Ginn, Barrie Maskell, Masami Kuwashima, Mo Harness and Roger Williamson. Tony Brise and Roger Williamson were particularly impressive: they won many races, both in Britain and on the Continent, Williamson taking the Shell Super Oil F3 Championship.

In Formula Two, the cars were in less capable hands and no results of any consequence were obtained. A 2-litre sports car was also built in 1972; one example was taken to Japan by Tetsu Ikuzawa, but few others were built and the model achieved no great success in the 1972 season.

For 1973, the monocoque chassis of the single-seater was updated and a number of new models were sold for F2 and F3 racing. In Formula Two, all the Ford-powered cars were at a disadvantage against the might of the BMW engines, but Reine Wisell won the Nürburgring round of the European F2 Championship in a GRD 273, while other customer cars, in the hands of Dahlquist, Kazato, Nilsson, Gunnarsson, Vonlan-

Top left: the 1972 Formula Two GRD 272 in action

Top right: the 1973 GRD 273 F2 car. Note that for that year, a much wider nose has been fitted

Above: Roger Williamson in his all-conquering GRD 372 F3 machine sponsored by Wheatcroft Racing

Left: Tetsu Ikuzawa of Japan driving the Formula Two GRD 273

then and McInerey, picked up a few minor placings.

Fewer F3 cars were sold in 1973, but Alan Jones in his GRD 373 did extremely well in the John Player F3 Championship, winning the rounds at Mallory Park, Zandvoort and Oulton Park, and taking several other good placings to finish a very close second in the Championship to Tony Brise's March.

In the European 2-litre Sports-Car Championship, Australian Dave Walker drove a GRD S73, but could seldom get to grips with the Lolas and Chevrons, his best placing being fourth at Imola.

Development had suffered during 1973, because too many customers had bought cars, the works not being able to service or develop these as snags were found. GRD's most prominent customer, Tom Wheatcroft, who was running an F2 car for Roger Williamson, decided to change to a March, while Dave Walker, the promising Australian, suffered a bad accident on the road which kept him out of racing for a long time. The company was also badly affected when the DART

Right: in 1973, GRD entered the 2-litre sports car class with their S73 machine. It was no match for the Lolas and Chevrons, however.

Below: Roger Williamson's highly-successful GRD 372 F3 model which is now on display in Tom Wheatcroft's Donington Museum

racing team, which was to have run GRDs, pulled out of motor racing.

The fuel crisis, towards the end of 1973, and the generally poor economic climate restricted sales of 1974 models. The single-seaters were all redesigned to have their radiators mounted at the front of the car instead of beside the chassis and the new suspension was designed so that it could be fitted to earlier models by customers. Although only ten new cars were delivered in the early part of 1974, the factory had been busy updating earlier cars with the new suspension, radiator and body parts.

The three main models in 1974 were the 274 for F2 at £5852 without engine or gearbox, the B74 for Formula B or Atlantic at £4466 less engine and gearbox, and the 374 for Formula 3 at £3846 less engine and gearbox. GRD were working on a Formula 5000 model for introduction late in 1974 and were also diversifying into boat building and general engineering. MT

Green Monster / WORLD OF SPEED

HIGH-SPEED MONSTER

Art Arfons became interested in drag racing by accident. A few years later, he became the fastest man on wheels in the world

Above: Art Arfons, one of the great names in the world of land-speed-record breaking

Above right: front and rear views of the crude but effective *Green Monster* record breaker of Art Arfons. The machine was fitted with a J79 engine taken from a Hustler jet bomber. The engine produced 17,500 shaft horsepower and the front suspension was taken from a 1937 Lincoln

ARTHUR EUGENE ARFONS was born near Akron, Ohio, in 1926. He was the son of a chicken-feed miller and had a brother, nine years his senior, called Walter. Although both brothers became keen amateur flyers, neither showed any interest in any form of motor sport until 1953, when Art happened upon a drag meeting while taking his family for a ride in the car. On his way to the local airport, he found that the road was blocked off and, on investigation, saw strange machines thundering down the tarmac. He was immediately impressed and went straight home to tell Walter about it.

In the space of a week, the brothers built their own car so that they could compete in the following Sunday's meeting. This, the first *Green Monster*, was aptly named. It was a real Heath-Robinson contraption, using a 1940 Oldsmobile engine sitting in part of the chassis from an Allis Chalmers tractor, this, in turn, resting on one aircraft wheel and two Packard wheels. The 'green' part of the name came from the surplus tractor paint used to daub the assembly.

Not surprisingly, this first *Green Monster* was not the quickest of the machinery around, managing only a quarter-mile terminal speed of 85 mph—to the amusement of the brothers' fellow competitors. So much fun was made of Art and Walt that they became determined to build a new, more sophisticated car.

Green Monster mark two fulfilled this ambition and gave the brothers considerable success. As Walt and Art became technically more competent and gained drag-racing experience, they built a whole series of *Green Monsters*, each more sophisticated than the last, and consequently more successful.

Drag racing is an obvious step towards a land-speed record attempt: it involves getting as much speed from a car in a straight line over a measured distance. By 1960, Art had built a jet-engined dragster, with which he gave demonstration runs at drag meetings around the USA. In the middle of that year, he and Walt took the car to Bonneville Salt Flats for a try out on salt, the reward being a run at 342 mph. At this time, the FIA ruling for the land-speed record was that all contenders had to use cars with at least two driven wheels. This excluded the pure-jet cars, although Donald Campbell used a gas turbine in his *Bluebird* so, for an attempt on the record, Art built a new *Green Monster*—a very simple machine with an Allison V12 aircraft engine mounted at the rear of the chassis.

By this time, Art and Walt had parted company. Neither was prepared to divulge the reason, but both were very keen on cracking the land-speed record, held since 1947 by the late John Cobb's Railton Mobil Special, with a figure of 394.19 mph. During August 1960, Art took his piston-engined machine to Bonneville, where four other teams were assembled in an effort to take the record.

Athol Graham was the first to attempt the record, but he crashed and was killed. Nathan Ostich gave up when the steering gear went wrong in his car. Mickey Thompson did a one-way run at well over 400 mph, but Challenger broke a drive shaft on the return trip. Art Arfons only got as far as a test run in *Green Monster*, because a transmission bearing failed during this session. Arfons decided that the days of piston engines and driven wheels for record-breaking were over and went away to think about his next move. Donald Campbell was the last to attempt the record in August 1960 and he suffered an enormous accident at high speed, being lucky enough to escape from the wreck with only minor injuries.

Art Arfons went back to his regular drag-racing career; in 1961, he shattered the 200 mph mark from a standing start through a quarter-mile, with a figure of 209 mph, and in 1963 he bettered this with 238 mph.

1964 was the year of the successful land-speed-record attempts. Campbell finally broke John Cobb's

WORLD OF SPEED / Green Monster

17-year-old best with a speed of 403.1 mph in his rebuilt *Bluebird* but, just prior to this, Craig Breedlove had raised the mark to 407.45 mph, in his jet-powered car, a record recognised by the Fédération Internationale de la Motorcycliste. Walt Arfon's *Wingfoot Express*, which had a Westinghouse J46 jet engine, soon raised this record to 413.2 mph in the hands of Tom Green. The FIA still did not recognise jet-engined cars, but Walt knew that his was the fastest machine on wheels, and once again the FIM were happy with the car.

As soon as Art heard about his brother's new achievement, he accelerated the construction of his own new *Green Monster*, using an enormous J79 engine, taken from a Hustler bomber. This car's engine produced 17,500 shaft horsepower and was simply attached to a basic frame and covered with a body. Front suspension was taken from a 1937 Lincoln, being a rigid axle, and was mounted on hydro-pneumatic struts; at the rear, the suspension was from a Ford truck. Following Donald Campbell's example, Arfons fitted a large tail fin to give the car good lateral stability and he added an airfoil at the front to prevent lift. The car's tiny wheels were fitted with special tyres made by Firestone, who sponsored the project. The *Green Monster*, which was basically a jet engine on wheels, made room for Arfons in a small cockpit to the left of the engine. Its aerodynamics left a lot to be desired, but it cost only £6000 to build.

On his first run, on 5 October 1964, Arfons managed 396.4 mph, but on his return run he raised the jet engine's boost and clocked a sizzling 479 mph to average 434.02 mph. Afterwards, Arfons said that he had been using only sixty per cent boost, so there was plenty in hand.

Two days later, Craig Breedlove raised the record to 526.28 mph with his *Spirit of America*, despite crashing into a salt lake after crossing the line, but Art was not beaten yet. Twelve days after this, he took *Green Monster* out again and, using only two miles instead of four or five to run up to the measured mile, he clocked 515.98 mph on his first run. He stepped up the boost for the return, knowing that he would have to be quicker, and went through the mile at an incredible 559.18 mph to record an average of 536.71 mph.

During October 1964, the FIA finally decided to recognise jet-engined cars as contenders for the land-speed record, so *Green Monster* became the first holder of that record.

Craig Breedlove built a new car, *Sonic 1*, for 1965 and raised the mark to 555.483 mph. Although *Sonic 1* used the same type of engine as *Green Monster*, it was more sophisticated, but this did not deter the brave Art Arfons, who took his machine out again five days later. Without using full boost, and still using his short run-up, Arfons clocked an average of 576.553 mph for the two runs. However, as he passed the mile post on the return run, his offside rear tyre burst—at over 600 mph. The flailing tyre ripped off one of the

braking parachutes, smashed the electrical firing mechanism and filled the cockpit with smoke, but Arfons coolly removed the cockpit canopy to regain vision, released the remaining parachute and steered the car back on course—all at 550 mph. Despite this courageous effort, Art only held the record for a few days, for Breedlove broke the 600 mph barrier on 15 November 1965 at 600.601 mph.

Arfons was still determined to get back the record, so in 1966 he rebuilt *Green Monster*, fitting new rear suspension, rebuilding the body to give a better aerodynamic shape with decreased lift, and strengthening many components. On 17 November 1966, he made his attempt on the record. The car proved to be very fast, but at around 610 mph, on the first run, a front wheel bearing broke up and seized, sending the *Green Monster* into a series of end-over-end rolls. Art Arfons reacted quickly, as all the wheels flew off, and released the braking parachute. This helped to stop the somersaulting, but the *Green Monster* settled on one side and slid a mile or so along the flats before coming to rest, albeit in many pieces.

All that was left after this was the driver's cockpit, with the hood blown away. Miraculously, Arfons escaped with only a badly abraded face, a few cuts and a slightly damaged eye. He said he would return, but he never did, plans for a new car being shelved after the advent of Gary Gabelich's rocket-propelled *Blue Flame*, which set the record at 630.388 mph in October 1970. He talked of building a jet or rocket-powered boat, but he gave up even his drag-racing activities when he crashed during a demonstration run, in 1971, killing three people. MT/IW

Above: the cockpit of *Green Monster* showing the many dials needed for a jet-engined machine. Once, while travelling at over 550 mph, the cockpit filled with smoke. Fortunately, Arfons did not panic. He simply removed the cockpit canopy to regain vision, released his emergency parachute and steered the car back on course

Above left: Arfons demonstrates *Green Monster* on an airfield runway during a visit to Britain

Grégoire / THE GREAT CARS

THE COMPANY THAT DIED WITH ITS FOUNDER

The Grégoire company has a varied history. They produced everything from single-cylinder runabouts to advanced luxury tourers and racing cars

FOUNDED IN 1903, the Grégoire company of Poissy, Seine-et-Oise, France, came into the motor industry with all the delicacy of a reluctant bather testing the water with his big toe. Their initial range—an 8 hp single-cylinder, a 12 hp twin and a 20 hp four—was produced for only a matter of months, apparently to get the feel of the motor business, before being replaced with a more refined range of voiturettes.

The most famous of the new models, which appeared for the 1905 season, was the 8 hp twin, which had a pressed-steel chassis, swept in at the front in the very latest manner to give a tight turning circle, a Panhard type of change-speed gear, and shaft drive. The chassis ran on ball bearings throughout, and there were both internal and external contracting brakes on the rear.

The engine had side valves and thermosyphon cooling, with Bassé-Michel Nilmelior high-tension

Left: the Grégoire 8 hp model of 1906. It was fitted with an 1106 cc twin-cylinder engine

Below: Civelli de Bosch and his Grégoire before the start of the 1905 Concourse des Voiturettes

magneto ignition (there was also a battery and coil ignition for use as an alternative).

It was, in fact, a very refined light car, although its competition début, in the first Coupe de l'Auto race of 1905, was less than distinguished.

Alongside this model, Grégoire offered a 15 hp four-cylinder, again with shaft drive. There was a racing version of this model, which competed in the 1905 Circuit des Ardennes; Tavenaux's car took second place in his class in this event. Tavenaux and Civelli de Bosch were entered for the 1906 French Grand Prix in bigger, 7.4-litre machines with overhead valves, but only one started, and even then failed to survive the first lap.

There were further attempts to race the little twin in voiturette events, but it was as a touring model that this car became famous, its combination of quality and modest price—it cost £180 in chassis form—ensuring its survival in the sales lists until 1912. There was even a 'racing model', shown at Olympia in November 1907, which cost 195 guineas complete with body and large petrol reservoir. Up to 1909, the marque's output had consisted entirely of two four-cylinder models, but

Above: the 4-cylinder Grégoire of 1908. It was fitted with a 2212cc motor developing 18bhp

Left: Civelli de Bosch in action in his twin cylinder Grégoire during the 1905 Concourse des Voiturettes

Below: the attractive 14/20 HP phaeton model produced during 1908

at the Olympia show that year, the new 18/24 hp six was exhibited. The chassis was suspended on three-quarter elliptic springs at the rear, presumably to give a soft ride for the carriage trade, the cylinders were cast in pairs, and the most positive thing that the English concessionaires could find to say about the car was that it was 'very strong'.

'In addition,' added *Country Life*, 'there is promised early next year a single-cylinder model at a very low price'.

The low-priced single did not, however, materialise until 1912, and then presumably as a stop-gap replacement for the 8 hp twin—known as the Dumont-Grégoire, this car was actually built by a company at Asnières. It had a massive long-stroke engine and a curious friction transmission which offered nine speeds forward, plus reverse. Fortunately, it died young,—neither the gods nor the motoring public seem to have loved it at all.

More seriously, Grégoire had developed an overhead-camshaft engine in 1911, although this was

intended for a racing motorboat, and were working on four-carburettor, hemispherical-combustion-chamber racers in 1912, although these did not appear on the circuits. Instead, conventional sidevalve racers were entered in the Coupe de L'Auto—and failed to last the distance. Their only remarkable feature was a dual-ratio back axle. However, one of these cars, driven by Porporato, won the Coupe de la Sarthe in 1913, but as the all-conquering Peugeots did not take part in that event, it was a somewhat hollow victory

The most famous of the Edwardian Grégoires appeared around this time: this was the new 16/24, with a monobloc engine with a bore of 80 mm and a stroke of 160 mm. With four forward speeds, it was regarded as a somewhat sporting mount by most enthusiasts: the Grégoire company had, it seems, other ideas for, in 1912, they announced one of the most extraordinary cars of all time, the *Triple Berline*, based on an extended 16/24 chassis. The Berline, had a body like three little stagecoaches which had run into one another, a switchback roof and elegant curtains to all its windows (which had glazing bars dividing them into four panels each. It was, in fact, an early essay at producing a motor caravan type of vehicle. As a complete contrast, Grégoire also produced some very advanced saloon bodies around the same time.

Above: the Grégoire company made its name producing good quality motor cars. Typical of the make is this superb 1910 model seen at a recent veteran and vintage owners meeting

Left: forerunner of the famous Triple Berline was this 1910 16/24 hp Berline. Note the unusual body styling which looks rather like two coaches joined into one

Another advanced idea of the period—although the company could not take credit for it—was a pioneering use of aluminium pistons in a 16/24 belonging to that ingenious inventor Dr A. M. Low; his installation, in fact, predated that of W. O. Bentley's DFP.

There was also a sporting 14/20, which appeared in 1913; this formed the basis of the company's post-war production, although at the 1919 Motor-Show, what purported to be a Grégoire-Campbell was on the Grégoire stand. In fact, this was a 3-litre Bignan-Sport, which was at that time being built under the same roof at Poissy as the Grégoire proper.

Grégoire entered a team of racers for the 1920 Indianapolis 500; these had horizontal valves operated by exposed pushrods driven from camshafts mounted outside the crankcase, but a shipping strike killed their chances before the start.

The touring model gained overhead valves in 1921, but the firm's impetus was running out, and it only survived the death of its founder in 1923 by a few months. The last car to bear the Grégoire name was an imposter, in any case. It was an 1100 cc ohv voiturette with a CIME engine, assembled at Maubeuge, Nord, by Les Établissements Jacques Hinstin, and the only Grégoire part was the badge. Britons knew this model as the Little Greg, but it was a poor swansong for a company that had built up a sizeable reputation for quality. DBW

THE GREAT CARS / Grégoire

A MAN OF MANY TALENTS

Jean A. Grégoire was a man of many talents among them being car manufacturing, writing and playing music

JEAN A. GRÉGOIRE, BORN IN 1899, was not related to the manufacturer of the other car to bear this name, although when he was at school, he would claim that his uncle was the builder of the Grégoire cars to counter assertions that the company belonged to his father.

In fact, Grégoire *père* was a railway engineer who was convinced that his son should receive a thorough grounding in physics to fit him for any subsequent career he might choose, and accordingly gave the boy a choice between the École des Mines and the École Polytechnique for his final education.

Young Jean chose the Polytechnique where, apart from his academic achievements, he became a brilliant athlete. He served during World War I, took his doctorate in law after the Armistice, and started work in a textile factory. This had little attraction for him, so he resigned to go prospecting in Madagascar. On his return to France, Grégoire joined some friends to run an automobile business in Versailles. There he began racing an Amilcar and a Bugatti for fun; he also met Pierre Fenaille, a wealthy amateur engineer who was to have a great influence on Grégoire's subsequent career.

Fenaille suggested that Grégoire should join him in the construction of a light sports/racing car with the then-revolutionary feature of front-wheel drive. It was to be called the Tracta, from the French words *tracta avant*—'front-wheel drive'.

The prototype, nicknamed 'Gephi', after the phonetic sound of the initials of Grégoire and Fenaille, was built in the works of Langlois & Journod of Courbevoie, Seine, and first ran in the summer of 1926. Its 1100 cc SCAP engine was fitted with a Cozette supercharger, which gave the vehicle a 140 kph top speed; the front wheels had independent suspension.

First competitive outing for the new car was the Coupe de l'Armistice, a reliability trial for light cars and motorcycles run over a short circuit in the suburbs of Paris. The Tracta went up in flames, due to a short-circuit, and Grégoire only managed to put out the blaze by sacrificing an expensive travelling rug which had to be used as a fire blanket. Once the flames were out, the car was driven directly to the Lévy-St. Nom hill-climb in the Chevreuse Valley. It made the fastest time of the day!

Two Tractas were entered for the 1927 Le Mans 24 Hours' race, to be driven by Grégoire and Fenaille, but a pre-race crash in the team's Panhard support car eliminated Fenaille, and nearly put Grégoire out of the running. With his head swathed in bandages beneath his crash helmet, Grégoire managed to qualify in the event, averaging 48 mph over the 24 hours.

Backed by Fenaille senior, Grégoire built several hundred Tracta cars between 1927 and 1934. Power units included 1100 and 1600 cc SCAP engines, and 2.7-litre Continental and 3-litre Hotchkiss engines.

Mused Grégoire: 'I do not think the Société des Automobiles Tracta ever managed, no matter what the price was, to sell a car for more than its actual cost!'

The Tracta front-wheel drive layout was widely copied under licence, although it seems that Grégoire did not always receive the appropriate payment, especially from German companies.

In 1936, he devised a diecast monocoque construction system which was tested on an Adler and which went into production on the Hotchkiss-built Amilcar Compound models launched at the 1937 Paris Motor Show. These 1185 cc front-wheel-drive machines had all-round independent suspension, as well as the Alpax light-alloy unit-constructed body/chassis unit. However, they were short-lived, for Amilcar ceased production during 1939.

Refusing to work for the occupying German forces during World War II, Grégoire was 'demobilised' by Hotchkiss. Working in secret, he designed the Aluminium-Francais Grégoire, a tiny four-seater 600 cc flat-twin car whose Alpax integral chassis/body framing was obviously based on the Amilcar Compound. In fact, this model was never built under Grégoire's name, although there were ambitious, but short-lived, schemes to build it under licence in England as the Kendall, backed by the MP Denis Kendall, and in Australia as the Harnett-Grégoire. However, Panhard used the design as the basis of their Dyna range, which was a far more successful venture.

There was also a 2-litre Hotchkiss-Grégoire flat-four, available in small numbers from 1952–55. The American Kaiser-Frazer of 1946 was originally to have followed this design under Grégoire licence.

In 1952, the SOCEMA-Grégoire gas-turbine car appeared at the Paris Salon; heresy of heresies, it had rear-wheel drive! Its 100 bhp Cematurbo power unit drove through a Cotal electric gearbox, but the venture was still-born.

Grégoire returned to his traditional muttons in 1956 with a derivative of the Hotchkiss-Grégoire built under his own name in small numbers in his works at Asnières, Seine; these cars carried handsome two-seater coachwork by Henri Chapron, but faded from the buyers' lists around 1962.

Most successful of Grégoire's post-war designs, it seems, was his variable-rate suspension system, which was adopted, among others, by the Renault company.

In any case, cars played only a part in the well-rounded life of J. A. Grégoire, for it is recorded that he was an authority on wine and mushrooms, a connoisseur of fine art and a competent pianist. And an author, whose autobiography *l'Aventure Automobile* (published in England as *Best Wheel Forward*) is one of the classics of motoring literature.   DBW

Above: in 1956, Jean A. Grégoire produced the two-seater sports car derived from the earlier Hotchkiss-Grégoire. It was fitted with a flat-four-cylinder, 2200 cc engine developing 130 bhp. The coachwork was by Henri Chapron. The car had faded from the buyer's lists by 1962

A stranger in his own country

MOTOR RACING IS RICH in 'characters', and few greater characters ever existed than America's Masten Gregory. Yet Gregory could not have looked less like a racing driver had he tried. He was short and skinny, wore thick horn-rim spectacles and spoke with a slow Kansas City drawl that seemed to come from the depths of his cowboy boots. Nevertheless, he had a long and varied racing career and was one of the first Americans to establish himself on the European motor-racing scene.

Gregory was born on 29 February 1932 to reasonably wealthy parents. At the age of fifteen, he unofficially began his motor-sport career by borrowing one of the family cars late at night and drag racing it through the streets of Kansas City. Two years later, he married and set up home in Mission Hills, Kansas. It was here that his interest in motor racing was fully developed. His brother-in-law, Dale Duncan, was involved in racing midget cars and it was he who introduced Gregory to the sport. Shortly afterwards, Gregory's father died, leaving him sufficient capital to begin a racing career.

His début, driving a Mercury-engined Allard J2X in a SCCA 50-mile event, was hardly successful. After five hair-raising laps (a typical Gregory trademark throughout his career), the engine blew a gasket and he retired. However, the racing bug had bitten hard and the Mercury engine was soon exchanged for a 325 bhp Chrysler motor. Together, he and Duncan set off to race in the 1953 Sebring 12-hour event. Again the car failed and he returned home with the Allard and a brand-new Jaguar C-type in tow. Driving the Allard, he gained his first victory at Golden Gate Park in 1953, before switching to the C-type in which he scored several good placings during the season.

At the beginning of 1954, he decided to campaign in Europe and bought a 4.5-litre Ferrari. Co-driving with Biondetti, he was fourth in the Reims 12-hour, 3rd at Lisbon and 1st at Aintree and Nassau. His success inspired him to remain in Europe and for 1955, he acquired a 3-litre Ferrari. He followed thirds at Bari and the Eiffelrennen with a first at the Lisbon Grand Prix and also scored a class victory at the TT, co-driving a Porsche Spyder with fellow American Carroll Shelby. His best showing the following year was a class victory at Nassau.

Up to this stage, Gregory's career had been concentrated around the European sports-car-racing scene. In 1957, however, he turned his talents to single-seaters and signed for the Italian Scuderia Centro Sud team. Driving their Maserati 250Fs, he had his best season ever, finishing fourth at Pau, fourth at Pescara, fourth in the Italian GP and third in the Monaco GP. He completed every race he started in and finally gained sufficient points to be classified fourth in the World Championship table. He did not neglect his sports-car career, however, and finished second to Fangio in Portugal.

The following year, 1958, Gregory joined the Scottish Ecurie Ecosse team, but had a dismal season. He finished few races and showed little of the previous season's form and was lucky to survive a huge accident at Silverstone in which he managed to destroy the team's Lister Jaguar. In spite of this, he was signed to drive as number three to Jack Brabham and Bruce McLaren in

Above: Masten Gregory throws the giant AC Cobra around the tricky Targa Florio circuit during the 1964 event

the works Cooper F1 team for 1959. This was the year that saw the tiny rear-engined Coopers victorious, the World Championship title eventually going to the Australian, Brabham. Despite being eclipsed by his two team mates, Gregory managed a third in the Dutch Grand Prix and a second in the Portuguese Grand Prix. The problems of running a three-car works team, however, proved to be too much for the Cooper organisation and so, at the end of 1959, Gregory was dropped. By this time, Gregory had acquired a reputation for crashing and none of the leading Formula One teams would have him on their books, so he rejoined the Scuderia Centro Sud. Success eluded him, however, and he returned to his first love, sports-car racing, signing for the American Camoradi Racing Team to drive their new, but unreliable, Maserati Tipo 61s. His greatest success during these lean years was a superb victory at the 1961 Nürburgring 1000 kilometre event, co-driving the 'Birdcage' Maserati 61 with Camoradi patron 'Lucky' Casner. In 1963, he captured the Players 200 at Mosport Park, but the interim year, spent driving a Formula One Lotus for the UDT Laystall team, proved frustrating and fruitless.

Perhaps his greatest victory was his win in the 1965 Le Mans 24-hour endurance race, an event he had been given little hope of winning. His co-driver was a young Austrian, Jochen Rindt, who, like Gregory at that time, was burdened with a reputation as a car wrecker. Their machine was a private Ferrari 275LM, entered by the North American Racing Team, a team whose reputation for reliability and efficiency was, until then, conspicuous by its absence. Nevertheless, the two held their car together and outlasted all the more highly fancied works runners to take a surprise victory. Gregory's critics were silenced. Their allegations of poor eyesight and dangerous driving were further battered by Gregory's superb drive in the 1965 Indianapolis 500, a form of racing unfamiliar to the by-now 'European-ised' American. After qualifying 31st on the grid, he electrified the huge crowd by moving up to fifth place by lap 43, eventually being forced to retire through engine failure.

Thereafter, Gregory returned to Europe, but his appearances became fewer and further between. In 1969, he won the Österreichring sports-car event in a Porsche 908 and in 1970 he and Toine Hezemans drove a works Alfa Romeo T33 to third place in the Sebring 12-hour race. His last year of racing was 1971, when he drove for the Alfa Romeo team. Gregory, who speaks several European languages fluently, was living in Holland in 1974, where he was in the diamond business. MW

This magnificent four-color encyclopedia is brought to you by Columbia House in cooperation with Orbis Publishing Ltd., one of Great Britain's most enterprising publishers. Rather than change any of the encylopedia's authoritative international automotive text, we have included a glossary of terms that will give you immediate American equivalents, a conversion table for the international metric system, and a conversion table for equivalent monetary values.

Glossary

BRITISH	AMERICAN	BRITISH	AMERICAN
Aerial	Antenna	Motor	Engine
Aluminium	Aluminum	Number plate	License plate
Apron	Skirt	Overrider	Bumper guard
Big-end	Rod (conrod) bearing	Paraffin	Kerosene
Blower *(colloquial)*	Supercharger	Parking brake	Parking lock
Bonnet	Hood	Petrol	Gasoline, "gas"
Boot	Trunk	Petrol pump	Gasoline or fuel pump
Brake servo	Power brake	Production car	Stock car
Bulkhead	Firewall	Propellor shaft	Drive shaft
Capacity	Displacement	Quarter light	Door vent
Carburetter; carburettor	Carburetor	Rear lamp	Tail light
Check strap	Door stop	Rear seat squab	Rear setback or backrest
Clutch release bearing	Clutch throwout bearing	Reverse lamp	Back up light
Control box	Voltage regulator	Roof lamp	Dome light
Crown wheel and pinion	Ring gear and pinion	Saloon	Sedan
Cylinder block	Cylinder crankcase	Scuttle	Cowl
Dip switch	Dimmer switch	Selector rod	Shift bar
Door pillar	Door post	Servo-assisted	Power assisted
Drop arm	Pitman arm	Side lamp	Parking light
Drop-head	Convertible	Side member	Side rail
Dynamo	Generator	Spanner	Wrench
Epicylic gearbox	Planetary gearbox	Sparking plug	Spark plug
Exhaust silencer	Muffler	Starting handle	Crank handle
Facia panel	Dashboard	Steering column	Steering post
Gear lever	Gear shift lever	Steering relay	Steering idler
Gearbox	Transmission	Stub axle	Steering knuckle
Gearbox housing	Transmission casing	Sump	Pan
Gearchange	Gearshift	Swivel pin	King pin
Glassfibre	Fiberglass	Toe board	Toe pan
Grease nipple	Grease fitting	Track	Tread
Gudgeon pin	Piston or wrist pin	Track rod	Tie bar or track bar
Half shaft	Axle shaft	Two-stroke	Two-cycle
Handbrake	Parking brake	Tyre	Tire
Hose clip	Hose clamp	Valance	Rocker panel
Ignition harness	Ignition set	Wheel arch	Wheelhouse or housing
Kerb	Curb	Wheel brace	Wheel wrench
Layshaft	Counter shaft	Windscreen	Windshield
Main shaft	Output shaft	Wing	Fender
Marque	Brand, make	Wishbone	A-arm; Control arm
		Works	Plant, factory

Metric Equivalents
(Based on National Bureau of Standards)

Length

Centimeter (Cm.)	= 0.3937 in.	In.	= 2.5400 cm.
Meter (M.)	= 3.2808 ft.	Ft.	= 0.3048 m.
Meter	= 1.0936 yd.	Yd.	= 0.9144 m.
Kilometer (Km.)	= 0.6214 mile	Mile	= 1.6093 km.

Area

Sq. cm.	= 0.1550 sq. in.	Sq. in.	= 6.4516 sq. cm.
Sq. m.	= 10.7639 sq. ft.	Sq. ft.	= 0.0929 sq. m.
Sq. m.	= 1.1960 sq. yd.	Sq. yd.	= 0.8361 sq. m.
Hectare	= 2.4710 acres	Acre	= 0.4047 hectar
Sq. km.	= 0.3861 sq. mile	Sq. mile	= 2.5900 sq. km.

Volume

Cu. cm.	= 0.0610 cu. in.	Cu. in.	= 16.3872 cu. cm.
Cu. m.	= 35.3145 cu. ft.	Cu. ft.	= 0.0283 cu. m.
Cu. m.	= 1.3079 cu. yd.	Cu. yd.	= 0.7646 cu. m.

Capacity

Liter	= 61.0250 cu. in.	Cu. in.	= 0.0164 liter
Liter	= 0.0353 cu. ft.	Cu. ft.	= 28.3162 liters
Liter	= 0.2642 gal. (U.S.)	Gal.	= 3.7853 liters
Liter	= 0.0284 bu. (U.S.)	Bu.	= 35.2383 liters
Liter	= $\begin{cases} 1000.027 \text{ cu. cm.} \\ 1.0567 \text{ qt. (liquid) or } 0.9081 \text{ qt. (dry)} \\ 2.2046 \text{ lb. of pure water at } 4\ \text{C} = 1 \text{ kg.} \end{cases}$		

Weight

Gram. (Gm.)	= 15.4324 grains	Grain	= 0.0648 gm.
Gram	= 0.0353 oz.	Oz.	= 28.3495 gm.
Kilogram (Kg.)	= 2.2046 lb.	Lb.	= 0.4536 kg.
Kg.	= 0.0011 ton (sht.)	Ton (sht.)	= 907.1848 kg.
Ton (met.)	= 1.1023 ton (sht.)	Ton (sht.)	= 0.9072 ton (met.)
Ton (met.)	= 0.9842 ton (lg.)	Ton (lg.)	= 1.0160 ton (met.)

Pressure

1 kg. per sq. cm.	= 14.223 lb. per sq. in.
1 lb. per sq. in.	= 0.0703 kg. per sq. cm.
1 kg. per sq. m.	= 0.2048 lb. per sq. ft.
1 lb. per sq. ft.	= 4.8824 kg. per sq. m.
1 kg. per sq. cm.	= 0.9678 normal atmosphere
1 normal atmosphere	= $\begin{cases} 1.0332 \text{ kg. per sq. cm.} \\ 1.0133 \text{ bars} \\ 14.696 \text{ lb. per sq. in.} \end{cases}$

Approximate Values of the Pound (£)
in terms of U.S. Dollars ($)

1914-1919	$4.76
1935	4.90
1936	4.97
1937	4.94
1938	4.89
1939	4.46
1940-1949	4.03
1950-1967	2.80
1968-1970	2.40
1971-1972	$2.40/2.60
1972-Present	2.60/2.10